Cambridge –
As War Clouds
Roll By

By the same author:

Dew on My Feet
Pimbo
What Pimbo Did Next
Pimbo and Jenny in old Cambridge
Knock on Any Door
From Cambridge—one and all!
In the shadow of King's
Gentle Tales of Old Cambridge
Cambridge Tales of Mystery and Mirth
The Magic Book for Cats

Cambridge –
As War Clouds
Roll By

F. T. Unwin

ISBN 0 9505966 8 X
Published by F. T. Unwin, 9 Cockcroft Place, Cambridge.
Tel: Cambridge (0223) 352438
Printed and bound by The Burlington Press (Cambridge) Limited,
Foxton, Cambridge CB2 6SW
Tel: Cambridge (0223) 870266
Drawings by Frances Richardson,
49 Hauxton Road, Little Shelford, Cambridge

PREFACE

CAMBRIDGE – AS WAR CLOUDS ROLL BY

At long last! The book you have been waiting for!
Pimbo and Jenny return from the war: finding
post-war Cambridge steeped in – Food rationing,
utility furniture, clothing coupons, a scramble for
jobs, and lack of accommodation for its home-
coming heroes. Read of their heart-warming
adventures, as they: Move from lodging to lodging,
try one job after another in a quest to set up home,
and rear a family. The book is rich in anecdotes and
colourful characters. F. T. Unwin has the unique
record of having sold over 60,000 copies of his
books, from door-to-door.

CONTENTS

EAST ROAD BALLAD

I stood on the East Road roundabout to watch,
The noisy passage of motor-bikes and cars.
Begoggled faces, as though from Mars,
Speed by into a Cosmopolitan hotch-potch;
Until they reach a part of the Town,
Where only ghosts look down!

All at once, from my dream, I started,
For, encircling me in complete disarray,
Were people, and houses, from long since day;
Those I once knew, and with wrench had parted,
Standing in an aura, which gleams,
On faces seen in dreams.

Outside the old Drill Hall, I see lads in uniform,
The bugles sound, but the Railway of Death, remains,
There's no Jericho to conceal blood stains,
Only, loving friends to mourn.
Winton-Smith, nearby, sells sausages and pies,
And Hopkin's fish and chips, still fries!

Tram lines, as bulging veins, glisten in the Sun,
Reach up to Peak's warehouse, then terminate,
Carrying bedmakers, and plumber's mate.
George Hall's cafe, offers welcome tea and bun ;
For those in workless, desperate plight,
The White-Ribbon, settles for the night,

Sylvester's ices, Florrie Blake's fine fresh fruit,
The tiny shops near South Street,
Offer groceries, and week-end meat.
George Pope's music, jars against the flute,
The buzz of saws from Coulson's shop,
Silence the crack of whip on top.

East Road 'College', past Loker's school-house lane,
Had Kingdom, Baldry, Coleman and Mallett,
To teach emphatically on, how to 'spell it'
May be a future errand boys' domain;
But, worthy lads emerged from such a place,
Going there, was certainly no disgrace!

The totters cry, 'Rag, bone or bottle', fills the air,
To Bill Westerley, Ted Loates and bluff Tom King;
Poor mothers, for pennies, their cast-offs bring.
Dooley Hall, for a kiddy with a jam-jar to spare,
Exchanges it for a windmill whirl,
Sheer heaven, for a boy or girl!

Baptist Church, with Raymond Brown, tends its fold.
Summerlee, Northfield, and Kefford, ply their trade,
Collins, Kemp, Green and Scott, their razors parade.
Though named as such, a street is not paved with Gold.
Alas, now all is gone, my dream lies shattered.
I hope I've covered memories that mattered!

Yes, in East Road once lived characters galore,
Joe Day, Medcalfe, Bloy, Reynolds, memory to jog.
Barbrooke, Pearson, Granny Smith, and dear Molly
    Hogg.
McKay's, Curly Northfield, and many names more.

East Road, an artery, once pumping life into
    dilapidation,
Has, now, a pacemaker for its new generation!

Fred Unwin

CHAPTER 1

Vicarage Terrace

After the Second World War, Pimbo and Jenny set up home in a small terraced house in Vicarage Terrace; a street which boasted of being the first bombing casualty of the war. With the haunting thoughts of her childhood days spent in one Childrens' Home or another; Jenny had declared, "It's my own little place, my own back door key, and to please myself when I come or go!" — It didn't work out quite like that!

In his boyhood days, Pimbo had frequented the Vicarage Terrace area during his many excursions into the labyrinth of tiny passageways at the rear of the buildings. Porky and Arthur Loynes, Tigger Langford, Cherry Palmer and Archie Unwin, with many others, had enjoyed their games of 'Off' and 'Platters'. It was the mother of Pimbo's friend, Stan Minter, who introduced the newly-weds to their first nesting place, and their first landlady.

"You see, my dears!" she said kindly. "Mrs Northfield lives on her own, she's called 'Noah' by many people, I'm sure you'll get on well together. There's one thing, though, Noah is getting on in years, at times she gets confused — but, for the benefit of a place of your own, we expect you to keep a watchful eye on her — I live just up the street, Sturton Street, for that matter, so let me know should anything untoward crop up!"

The little house boasted of a small back kitchen, with a fire place. A tiny scullery with gas stove and sink, plus an outdoor toilet, completed the rear section of the house.

Pimbo and Jenny used the front room facing the street as their living quarters, with a back bedroom, share of the scullery and toilet making up their agreed share of the home.

Their first evening seemed sheer bliss. With the curtains drawn, a paraffin stove for warmth, and the wireless pumping out the latest Henry Hall tunes, a far cry from the army days of both, during which they had experienced all that war-time shortages could offer.

From her old ATS bag, Jenny produced a lovely antimacassar, the ornamental section being of pure silk. "For years I've been awaiting the time when I could use this in my own home!" She held it up to the light in order to savour its beauty still further. "It was a parting present from an old ATS chum, she was set on being an old maid!"

Jenny moved across to the old sofa, taking up the antimacassar owned by Noah, which had seen far, far better days; she folded it neatly, placing it on the sideboard; Jenny replaced it with her own, then side by side, the happy couple viewed the change.

"It makes the sofa seem new!" laughed Pimbo. "A crowning feature of our new life together!"

"And no Brylcreem to spoil it, I remember your

mother telling me how you ruined the wallpaper with your greasy head — but, now, it's down to business!"

Producing a set of empty tea-tins, bought at a jumble sale, Jenny labelled them with, 'Rent', 'Gas', 'Coal', 'Insurance', 'Clothing' and 'Holidays'.

"I want to start on the right foot. I've too many bad memories of debt, and near starvation, and never having a penny to call my own. My poor old mum used to say, 'always put enough by to keep a roof over your head!' "

Pimbo smiled knowingly. During the war, after allowing his mother £1 weekly, he, through dint of not smoking or drinking, had come out of the Army with six hundred pounds. Purchasing clothes without dockets, filling up a bottom drawer with goods that had reached sky-high prices through post-war shortages, was slowly eating into his savings — Jenny was wise in introducing her weekly saving tins.

A tap at the parlour door let in Mrs Northfield. A slight figure, with a type of cleft lip, giving her a rather nasal whine to her voice, stood viewing the adjustments the happy couple had made to their furnished accommodation. Rather crossly, she scurried across to the side-board, snatching up her rejected antimacassar. "I don't want you to make too many changes — after all, you must think yourselves lucky in getting a roof over your heads!"

Jenny smiled. "Of course, Mrs Northfield. But, I'm sure you understand. I have a suitcase full of things which I've collected over the years, from the moment I met Pimbo — I just want to see some of them surface in the room I live in!" Glancing across to the mantel-piece, Jenny took stock of the old sepia framed photographs, which epitomised Noah's entire married life of struggle, ambitions, and fleeting moments of joy. Walking across to the old lady, Jenny kissed her gently on each cheek. "I promise not to make sweeping changes — but, remember, I too, have my life to fulfil!"

As Noah left the room, Pimbo put the kettle on for a cup of tea. "The ATS must have taught you a lot about handling tough situations. Do you know, Jenny, it's taught me a lesson, too. From now on, it's you the boss in the home, with me as the provider. I'll look out tomorrow for a job, our money won't last much longer — !"

A knock at the front door let in an old Army pal of Pimbo's. It was Len Palmer, who had been a bombardier to Pimbo's Troop Sergeant. Over a cup of tea, Len talked over the possibility of finding a job. Pimbo was realising all at once, the incongruity of having a responsible job in the Army — then to suddenly become a nobody, no rank, no qualifications, and little hope of achieving a like status as that of his Army career! Len was in the same boat — he'd come down from London, with his wife having left him from a 'Brief Encounter' type of flirtation. Len too, was looking for a fresh start, believing that in Pimbo, remembering their ways of 'winning' things in the Western Desert, might materialise in their setting up a new career for themselves.

Pimbo viewed Len thoughtfully; glancing at Jenny he caught a look in her eye which was saying: "look here, you were one of the earlier demobs, soon the others will be storming the labour market, you've had your desert-fling, now it's different, it's the both of us, a job, a house of our own, babies, and all the trappings of a happy marriage".

As he was thinking, a figure emerged from the kitchen, it was Mrs Northfield. She walked to the edge of the little table, then with both hands gripping its edge, with knuckles showing white under her tension, she stood staring at the ex-bombardier.

"I got your address from the Post Office!" Len stammered. "I'm sorry, I didn't know you had married. You've enough on your plate, I'm sure. Thanks for the tea, I'll be off now, my train leaves in half-an-hour!" Shaking hands with Pimbo, and a quick peck on Jenny's cheek, the bombardier moved away for ever from Pimbo's life!

Jenny was staring at Noah. "But you didn't knock, you came straight in on our privacy — you must have been listening?"

The landlady moved from the table, and sat on a chair slid under her by Pimbo. "Yes, I was listening! I've been living alone in this house since my hubby died, I've sat by my fire staring into the flames, and sometimes I see things. That young man's a good un, but it's up to him to find a way for *himself* — not to drag you down with him. You mustn't think too unkindly of old Noah — you're just like my children were at your age — it's just that I'd like to mother you!"

After Noah had gone back to the kitchen, the young newly-weds stared in silence at each other, then Pimbo relieved the tension. "Come on, Jenny, we've had enough drama for one day — we'll go for a walk, I haven't been around this area since before the war!"

At the top of Norfolk Street, leading into Burleigh Street, Pimbo spotted a large van with the name S. Silverman painted on its side. Heading a list of items for sale were the words in large capitals, 'ARMY SURPLUS'. Jenny, also spotting the van, tugged at his arm, then smiled. "There you are, Army Surplus — that's us, Pimbo. You see, we might yet be in great demand!"

"I don't want you to work!" said Pimbo, as they moved across into Burleigh Street. "With your gammy knee, a grim reminder of your ATS days, you'll have enough in hand to being a good housewife!"

The young couple stopped at the top of Adam and Eve Street; to Pimbo's surprise, the little terraced homes were still standing. A friend of his from the Territorial days, Bill Hamence, had a little house at the bottom, Pimbo expected that one day Bill would be moving into a new Council house.

As though reading his thoughts, Jenny broke in. "We must get our names down on the Council list, with our Army service we could be well up on the points system!" Turning back on to East Road, they made their way on to Mill Road, past the beloved Playhouse Cinema, past the Kinema, and through into Gwydir Street.

At the top of Sturton Street, looking down into Vicarage Terrace, they studied the cleared-away debris of half the little homes blasted by the German bomber on that specific moonlight night. Little did they realise that their married life would begin almost upon the ashes of those killed on that

fatal night. Jenny shrugged as Pimbo pointed out
the grim facts. "A life ends, just as a life begins!"
said Jenny. "We'll get back to our little haven, and
see how Noah's been getting on!"

As they entered the front room, in true woman-
ish style, Jenny gave a laugh, and pointed to the
top of the old sofa. In their absence, the landlady
had removed Jenny's smart antimacassar, replac-
ing it with her own well-worn hole-ridden replica.

Not to be outdone, Jenny rolled up Noah's
antimacassar, and replaced it with her own.
Looking across to Pimbo, she smiled wanly. "The
old gal is hanging on to her memories — we mustn't
be too hard on her, but, on the other hand, *we* are
paying the rent!"

Soon, with the curtains drawn, the blinds down,
and good tunes coming from the radio, the young
couple put behind them the teething problems of
moving in with an old lady. Both realised what a
different Cambridge they had come back to. It was
like a sleeping giant, gradually awakening from
dormancy into a different world, a time of dockets,
rationing, and job seeking. The novelty of returning troops was wearing off, funny little looks were
being given to shoppers who had recently been
demobbed, as though they might be using clandestine gained coupons.

"I'll try for a job tomorrow!" Pimbo was saying.
"There's one in the News, Tovey Transport require
a storekeeper. It carries a little status and maybe
lead me into something better — if I wait much
longer, the next demob categories will be out, jobs
will be harder to get!"

"You've only had two weeks holiday, I thought it

would be nice for us to be together a little longer —
but I'm with you — "

A sudden large thumping noise was coming from
the stairs which led up from Noah's kitchen.

As the incredible noise continued, the young
couple moved into the vicinity of the disturbance.
The door at the bottom of the stairs was wide open;
Pimbo, anxiously peeping into the semi-darkness,
was surprised at what he saw.

Noah was slowly making her way up to the top of
the stairs. At each stop she was lifting a huge
brown stone jar, similar to those used in the
whisky-brewing films of the American hill-billies.
It must have weighed several pounds when filled
with hot water, which Noah used as a very
primitive hot-water bottle.

Pimbo stepped in quickly, taking the stone jar
from the landlady, and moving it into the bedroom
used by Noah, overlooking the street. "I've used the
jar for years!" gasped the out of breath old lady.
"Each year I find it getting harder. Once I was able
to take it up in one go — but I'm afraid it's getting
too much for me!"

"From now on, you leave it to me!" put in Pimbo,
"otherwise you'll be shaking the foundations of the
house — it won't need a bomb to complete the
damage!"

Laughingly, the young couple went to their own
little bedroom at the rear of the house, overlooking
tin sheds, bicycle lined yards, and tiny gardens
defying poverty to interfere with their lustre of
colours.

Jenny was unpacking a bundle of sheets and
pillow-slips she had purchased at a Belfast Linen

"I don't want you to make too many changes — you're lucky in getting a roof over your heads!"

'Sale'. "At least we'll be sleeping in our own bed linen. Poor old Noah, bless her, would find it too much, changing the bed clothes each time we go out!" Pausing after her words, Jenny smiled across at Pimbo, who was dutifully folding back a sheet into the mattress. "Are you happy?" she asked of Pimbo, plaintively.

Pimbo, with the distance across the bed too much to indulge in anything other than a nod, smiled in approval. Jenny was doing wonders with the rationing. Two-penn'orth of corned beef, and ten-penn'orth of meat was his weekly portion of sustinence. Listening to the gossip in shopping queues made him realise that many of the people who had stayed at home during the war had gone through much more than the front-liners had imagined.

Jenny was pulling out from a suitcase a pretty bundle of curtain material. "From the 'Belfast', but I won't make them up yet, until we're settled in a real home!" she said puckishly. "One thing they taught me in service was to never waste material — good material too, Pimbo, should wash well, and it's lined, the sun won't fade the colours — !"

She stopped suddenly, as she realised that her young husband was lost in a harsh world of domesticity, antimacassars, curtains, Irish linen, and stone jar hot-water bottles. Other things were on his mind as they cuddled down to their first night under the roof of a small terraced house in Vicarage Terrace.

CHAPTER 2

Pimbo Obtains His
First Post-War Job

Tovey Transport, with its head office in St
Andrew's Street, was a firm run by Paddy Harris,
the local bus tycoon. Its main function was the
clearance of septic tanks, situated in rural areas,
where the sanitary arrangements had not yet
lived up to those of its town neighbours. A large
garage, housing a fleet of Bedford lorries, required
for this function, was situated in Northampton
Street — Pimbo, with a wage of five pounds
weekly, started work as stores clerk on that
particular Monday morning.

Mr Ransome, a small, gentle voiced man, whose
capacity was that of manager, met a rather
nervous Pimbo at the garage entrance. "You'll
soon settle in. The business is growing, we've a
large fleet of lorries to maintain, the thing is —
that stores equipment is getting expensive, we
must account for every nut, bolt and gasket — !"
Looking up at Pimbo, he smiled confidently.
"That's where *you* come in, replenish the stock,
keep stock cards up to date, and on Sunday's we

pay overtime for the mechanics to come in, you won't be in on this, but we expect you to keep a careful eye on the job-sheets!"

The first hour was spent on a careful survey of all the stock, an introduction to the three permanent staff, and a general discussion on lunch breaks, heating arrangements, and time-off.

At Mr Ransome's departure to head office, Pimbo looked ruefully around the large corrugated-iron building. The small stores at the end of the building was choc-a-bloc with motor accessories of every description. Hanging on the wall were scores of engine gaskets of all sizes and dimensions, Pimbo had never seen such queer shapes! Little pangs of doubt began to assail his conscience; in order to get the job, he'd told a few white lies about his stores experience during the war, no doubt his rank of Troop Sergeant had been instrumental on his securing the post — but — ?

A greasy, oil-stained mechanic, broke his thoughts. "Get me a manifold gasket, and a steering-knuckle, mate. I want to finish this job by dinner!"

Pimbo thought quickly. Lifting up the counter flap which gave access to the stores, he beckoned the mechanic through. "Help yourself, mate. I've an urgent list to send up to Mr Ransome — sorry, but it'll save time!"

As the mechanic pushed past him, Pimbo, although bent down over his stated 'list', watched from the corner of his eye where the mechanic had taken his required spares. The moment he returned to his awaiting vehicle, Pimbo wrote on gummed labels the names of the parts, and stuck them under their appropriate positions.

The thought of getting the sack on his very first day would be too much for Jenny to bear! What sort of husband would he turn out to be? "I'll be the bread-winner, you the little housewife!" No, he must stick at it — learn off by heart every blessed item of equipment — down to the smallest screw!

Mr Wilson, the oldest employee of the firm, caught Pimbo's eye as the young storekeeper gazed round the workshop. Walking up to Pimbo, he laid an oil-stained rag on the top of the counter. "I reckon you need a bit of help, son — been in the same boat myself in my apprentice days. I'm out of retirement really, worked at Moore's Engineering on Histon Road, most of my life, rebores, valve grinding, pistons, cam-shafts, you name them, the firm was tops — but a little baccy money doesn't come amiss — so here am I, still doing what I know best at with engines!"

Pimbo smiled gratefully. As he was about to reply, a smartly dressed man carrying a brief case entered the garage. "I'm from Jones & Secker, spare parts and tensile nuts and bolts — I call once a year!"

Noticing Pimbo's hesitant manner, the traveller hastily drew out an order book from his case, pointing at a commodity at the top of the list, he smiled at the young storekeeper. "I see that you are new here. I'll help you out — two gross of tensile bolts, two gross of nuts to go with them — that's your usual order — OK?"

At that moment, Mr Wilson beckoned Pimbo

across to a small cupboard. Excusing himself, Pimbo peered intently inside as the old engineer pointed to box-upon-box of tensile nuts and bolts, piled high to the top of the cupboard.

"Enough to last two or three years!" put in Mr Wilson. "Tensile means to withstand extra pressure, a good line, but this bloke gets away with it each year — we certainly need a storeman here — tell him to call again in two years' time!"

During the fifteen minutes stop for tea, Pimbo noticed that the old engineer seemed to be shunned by the other mechanics, he was drinking his tea in a corner by himself. Pimbo took his mug of strong tea across to the old fellow. "Thanks a lot. I heard them mention you as Bob, may I call you that? Seems that you're not too popular about here, what's gone wrong?"

Bob smiled. "It's the post-war era. Many are on the make, the war breeds a lot of sharp practice. At my age, *character* comes first. I don't see eye to eye with all of them. You see, one or two of them have their own cars — they come in on Sundays, make out their own job sheet — need I say more? I like you, you seem honest and willing to learn — I suggest that you take home the spare-parts manual, mug up the proprietary names, that way, you'll have it over the mechs because they know only the slang names!"

On his way home, cycling through Magdalene Street and into Bridge Street, Pimbo reflected on his first day at work. It seemed so different from the war years, when, owing allegiance to just his officer, very few problems arose; a snapped-out order, the old officer's cliche of 'Carry on,

Sergeant', would surmount any difficulty — but, this was Civvy Street!

On entering his little Vicarage Terrace lodgings, Pimbo was surprised by a weeping Jenny. "It's Noah, she's been getting at me, thinks I've stolen her sheets — go in and pacify her, I can't do any more, I've put up with her all day!"

Pimbo made a cup of tea — passing one to Jenny, he kissed her gently on the cheek. "We'll take a bit of cooling-off time, can't have my little wife upset — now can we? Old people become paranoid, forget where they put things — maybe she hasn't really lost them at all — !"

He stared at Jenny, who, almost glassy-eyed, was staring into space. She was thinking of being thrown out, they had no claim to tenancy, no proof in writing that they were anything more than interlopers — what a return to an England fit for heroes to live in!

Pimbo suddenly threw off the morbidity. Walking to a large side-board, he pulled out the top drawer. Noah kept most of her possessions in the three drawers of the sideboard. With Jenny calmer, the young newly-weds gradually emptied the drawers — at the bottom of the last drawer lay three single sheets.

Winking at Jenny, Pimbo carried them into the adjoining kitchen. Noah was lying on her sofa looking an abject picture of misery. "Your missing sheets, Mrs Northfield!" said Pimbo, with mock authority. "I trust you will never again accuse my wife of theft. You had stored them away — remember they are single sheets — we use double sheets!" The old lady stared at Pimbo, then at the sheets. "I'm sorry, I'm getting old and forgetful. I didn't mean to hurt the lass — but for all I knew – !"

Jenny now entered the kitchen with a steaming cup of Bovril. "There, now, let byegones be byegones, but I wouldn't steel a pin from you, my dear — would you like me to put the sheets back in the sideboard?"

Back once again in their own quarters, Pimbo related the day's happenings at work. Jenny laughed at the irony of it all — a real taste of civvy-street, even the ex-Troop Sergeant had to face the music!

"Seriously, though, we must keep our eyes open for another place!" put in Jenny, suddenly. "The old lady will get worse before she gets better, I don't want our few sticks thrown out on to the pavement!"

Pimbo shrugged. With both being ex-service personnel, points for housing acceptance were fairly high, but it would still mean months of waiting their turn for a place of their own. He smiled as he looked at across at Jenny; having a baby would, of course, hurry things along — but they *were* trying; even then a year's waiting seemed in the offing.

A knock at the door broke his thoughts, it was Mrs Anny Elwin, an aunt of Jenny's, whose first visit it was since Jenny's demob.

"So you're as snug as a bug in a rug in your little love nest?" chirped Anny, "thought I'd pop round to see you, Pimbo's mate told me all about you — now what about coming round to my place for a nice cup of tea and a chat — I've done my front room out, decorated right through, you'll love it!"

The appearance of Noah at the kitchen door, stood in an open-mouthed listening mood, prompted the young couple to agree; a curt look from Jenny told Pimbo that it was akin to moving from the frying pan into the fire!

Aunt Anny lived in a small terraced house on East Road, consisting of a basement kitchen, a front room at pavement level, and two bedrooms at the top floor of the house. Her husband, Frank, greeted Pimbo in an old soldier fashion. "The hero home from the wars, eh, Pimbo? But I've been doing my bit, Home Guard and all that!"

"You can make a nice pot of tea, Frank, while I take Jenny up to see the front room, just give me the key, you'll find it in the back of the clock!"

With the key firmly in her fat little hand, Anny led the way up narrow, almost perpendicular stairs, into a kind of hall-way leading to the front parlour. Jenny stared down at neatly folded newspapers laid firmly over the coloured linoleum which, like a Raleigh cloak, led them to the front-room door.

Slightly out of breath, Jenny's aunt thrust in the key, turned it sharply, and proudly threw back the parlour door. "There, what do you think? Saved up, right throughout the war, kept my coupons — worth it, wasn't it?"

Pimbo noticed at once more newspaper covering the carpet, a settee with two armchairs, each festooned with a neatly laid newspaper. He lifted up part of a newssheet, disclosing perfectly rounded seats, as though no-one had ever sat in them. The room, despite the newness of the decoration, smelt a little musty. "I use the room only on high days and holidays!" said Anny, as though reading Pimbo's thoughts. "Do you like the wallpaper, Jenny — it's washable you know!"

Nodding in appreciation, Jenny's gaze took in the little glass cabinets, the highly polished sideboard; with its knick-knacks collected from many years of married life. She thought of Noah's little place, and wondered how long it would be — ! She gazed up at the glass framed pictures, the Titanic, Queen Victoria, Harvest Home, and one of Anny and Frank on their wedding day. From the window outside, she could see Collins tea-shop and Parfitt's butchery.

"Tea's ready!" shouted Frank from the basement. Leaving Anny to lock up and replace the newspaper covers, Jenny and Pimbo joined Frank with the tea-tray.

"I've a nice overcoat!" said Frank suddenly. "Should fit you to a T. Bit too heavy for me, I've only worn it once!"

Jenny nudged Pimbo; who, realising how difficult it was going to be getting clothes with the meagre supply of clothing coupons given him on demob, agreed to try on the coat.

It was a nice shade of blue, melton cloth, with double pockets, he glanced into the wall mirror, the fit was perfect!

"Twelve pounds — cost me twenty!" put in Frank. "You can't be too flush with clothing coupons — so forget them, there, you've got a real bargain!"

At that moment Aunt Anny came into the basement. "I want you upstairs a moment!" she announced curtly. Frank dutifully followed, leaving the newly-weds alone in the basement.

Jenny, giving Pimbo a wink, listened a while at the bottom of the stairs, then turned to Pimbo. "It's Portia demanding her pound of flesh — just see if I'm not right!"

True enough, Frank, a little shamefacedly, slunk back into the kitchen. "I'm sorry, I was too quick about the coupons, Anny wants to get herself a new frock — she wants twelve coupons for the coat!"

On the way home, the young couple were laughing at the outcome of that particular day.

With their own domestic issues allowed for, Pimbo's thoughts went back to the decorated front room, the newspaper covering on both floor and furniture. As Jenny was saying, "Anny has worked hard all her life; Frank, with bad health, has been in and out of work. I suppose, Anny's front room, under lock and key, protected by the cheapest of coverings, was, to her, 'her secret garden', the outcome of a life's scraping and clawing!"

Pimbo smiled. "But she never mentioned our war service once. Never asked how we got on, never said how pleased she was that we returned safely, how come — she's your auntie?"

"I suppose we're to blame, really!" replied Jenny.

"We return from war, expecting to be acclaimed as heroes, but we forget that civilians, too, went through a hard time. You see, Anny, during the war, has proved herself capable of holding her own, and proud enough to show it off. What have

Mr Moore watched intently as the rep entered the store.

we got? Pimbo, we've got it all to do, I'd like a
chance to take someone round *my* home, I know
you would too, Pimbo. But, the day will come,
there'll be no newspapers on the floor, or the
armchairs, I want our home to be lived in!"

"And the clothing coupons?" laughed back Pimbo.

"It'll teach us that we'll never get something for nothing — I suppose Hitler found that out!" replied Jenny, giving Pimbo's arm an extra squeeze.

At that time a weekly ration was 4oz bacon and ham, 8oz sugar, 1/2d worth of meat (6p), 2oz tea, 4oz cheese, 8oz jam, 6oz fat, 2oz butter; 12oz sweets monthly; and one fresh egg every six weeks. Vegetables and salad food rationed only by scarcity!

CHAPTER 3

Another Move

Jenny was finding Noah becoming more and more confused. Each time Pimbo and she returned from an outing, the poor old girl had once again changed Jenny's antimacassar to that of her own. Then, too, anyone calling in to see the newly-weds would have to suffer a gawping landlady, ready to absorb titbits of gossip, or break in with irrelevant remarks.

Mrs Minter was very understanding when Jenny explained the situation to her. "I've another place in mind for you, my dear. My mother-in-law is getting old, she needs someone in the house when her daughter goes to work. It won't be the same as with Noah; Molly, that's my daughter-in-law, lives with her. Matter of fact, Molly will be in today. Pop round to see her, I've already explained about your little problem!"

Molly lived in Hooper Street, a short distance from Vicarage Terrace. The house, a typical terraced dwelling, was well built, and sported a front room, kitchen, scullery, and two bedrooms, with a small back garden.

Molly, a tiny red-faced woman, quickly put

Jenny at ease. "I'd love you to come in with us. You see, Mum's all right when I'm here, but I have to go out to work, my hubby died some years ago, the rent has to be found. You'd get a room at the back, a bedroom, and use of the scullery, all for a pound a week — to cover gas and electricity — do say you'll come, I really need a little break and company; by the way, we all call Mum, Granny Bumkins!"

Over a cup of tea, the bargain was sealed. Molly found it difficult to hide her pleasure. "Do you know, my dear, I feel jealous of you just starting out — and yet, it seems hard on your having to take over the role of an old lady's minder — but, one day, maybe you'll experience the real joys of a happy marriage — it wasn't for me, my dear!"

Jenny detected the slight welling of a tear at the corner of Molly's eye. She busied herself with pouring more tea, but Jenny wasn't to let it pass. "Tell me about it, my dear — I'm young enough not to know it all!"

Leaving Jenny to sugar the teas, Molly left the room, returning with a small cardboard box. "I'm sorry, Jenny!" she said softly, "I didn't mean to pull the dramatics!" Opening the lid of the box, she took out the top garment — it was a baby's matinee jacket. A lovely hand-knitted shawl followed, with tiny bootees, a dear little bonnet, and lots of beautiful undergarments, knitted with the dedication of a doting mother-to-be!

"It was still-born, a baby girl! It broke my heart, a year later my husband died. So it's me back with mother, in the house where I was born. By the way, you haven't met mother yet, I'll see if she's awake!" Packing away the little memories, Molly, now more

composed, led Jenny into the kitchen where her
mother sat, on a small sofa, next to an old-
fashioned stove, shiny with grate polish, and
throwing out a nice warming glow.

Granny Bumkins, a small, thin, old lady, with a
rasping voice, looked up as the couple entered the
room. "I haven't had my dinner yet, Molly, where
have you been? — I haven't eaten for days! And the
fire — you went to work, never lit the fire, you
didn't, had to light it myself — I've told the
policeman about you!"

Molly smiled at Jenny. "You see what it's been
like. I can't leave her. She gets to the front door,
wrenches open the bolt, whoever passes gets the
same message, 'No fire — no food'. She's been a
lovely mother, but there's a limit to what I can
stand — now you're coming, when I'm at work, I
shan't need to worry!"

Making the old lady comfortable, Molly turned to
Jenny. "Now, this husband of your's, what's he
like? I've heard a lot about him, used to live round
here when a child — Pimbo, what a funny name!"

Jenny smiled. "We were childhood sweethearts,
even joined the Army together. He's a good 'un,
roughed it as a kid, now he wants something a little
better. We're starting from scratch, bed linen, a
few things packed in drawers — but we don't want
to get into debt, so it'll be little by little!"

As Molly handed her mother a cup of tea, Jenny
thought of an incident about two days ago. Pimbo,
who had suffered from TB as a child, was still
rather thin; Jenny decided on giving him a
spoonful of cod liver oil and malt each day as he left
for work. On that **particular morning**, she'd

forgotten until he had just left the house. In her nightdress, clutching a slowly oozing spoonful of cod liver oil and malt, Jenny managed to stop him some way down the street. In full view of passing workmen, Pimbo was reluctantly fed his daily dosage. Thinking of the commercial, 'The Milky Bar Kid', he drolly remarked to his wife, "The neighbours will call me 'The Oil and Malt Kid' !"

The old lady had fallen asleep. Molly tidied the kitchen, then showed Jenny the room in which she would be living. It looked out into the small back garden, Jenny spotted the outside lavatory close to the back door. The room was cosy looking, the furniture — no great shakes — but sufficient for two young newly-weds to cut their teeth on!

"I'll take you to the bedroom, it's next to mine. The walls are thin, at two a.m., you'll probably hear mum calling me up, 'it's time to get up, Molly — it's time to get up', but, I take her down for a few minutes, then I tell her it's time for bed — a kind of tit-for-tat, but it gets me a few hours more sleep!"

Jenny smiled to herself. How many such like happenings were hid behind the little front doors of Hooper Street, peeping out into a busy thorough-fare of cosmopolitan inhabitants. Married life wasn't going to be all beer and skittles!

"There you are!" said Molly, suddenly. "I'll expect you here on Monday. By the way, I'm a bedmaker at Emmanuel, start work at seven, so Mum will need you to look in from then on — I get home about dinner time — you can have a nice cup of tea awaiting me!"

Returning to Vicarage Terrace, Jenny found Noah in tearful mood. Apparently, Mrs Minter had broken the news of Jenny's leaving. The old lady, really, was little more than a child in her behaviour — one moment in seemingly lucid brain, yet another time, confused and disorientated.

"Mrs Minter will see that are not left alone. The Welfare Service knows all about you — I'm sorry, but you can't blame us, Hooper Street rooms are bigger — we'll pop in to see you now and again!" Jenny did her best to soften the blow, she was glad to hear Pimbo coming in through the front door.

"I've got a ten-bob rise!" greeted her young husband. "Mr Ransome thinks I'm doing well, there's talk of our moving to better-class premises, and me with a proper office!"

Using Pimbo's euphoric condition as a spring board to explain the day's happenings, Jenny soon had him eating out of her hand. To her relief, Pimbo accepted the idea with relish. "It's tough on poor old Noah — but it's our life, one day it'll be our turn to be chaperoned — until then — !"

Jenny pointed out to Pimbo, that despite his ten shillings rise, she would have to think about taking a job. "You see, when everything is paid, we're left with just a quid to last us a week. Should we be lucky enough to get a Council house, that quid would be absorbed in extra rent, insurance, with higher gas and electricity bills. That doesn't allow for saving up for our first child — as for new clothes — well, it'll be jumble sales from now on!"

The post-war years were indeed bleak, with rationing, austerity furniture and clothing; things were nothing as good as the ex-soldiers blissful hopes of 'an England fit for heroes to live in'. Jenny, on that particular day, was all fight. "I'm paying rent, and I don't like those curtains!" Foraging in her old ATS bag, she yanked out a pair of sheets, which she had put by from her in-service days. "There, you can slip up to the Co-op, and bring back a packet of Drummer dyes — I'll kick off with a nice golden colour — my old mum used to dye anything she laid hands on!"

Pimbo was smiling as he walked through Smart's Row, then into Staffordshire Street, and up to the little corner shop Co-op. Jenny's being in service had helped immensely. She knew how to pinch and scrimp, "Cheapness is a false economy — get a good thing, it'll pay for itself in the end" she'd say, "Now, you take my old mum's next door neighbour. Always buying and changing her curtains. My old mum, bless her, used to say, 'If she bought two good pairs, they'd see her through her married life!' ".

Returning to Hooper Street, Pimbo found Jenny had taken down Molly's original curtains. His young wife had a sink full of water with which she mixed up the two sachets of Drummer's golden dye.

A shout from the kitchen sent Pimbo pell-mell to see what Granny Bumkins was up to! To his dismay, he found the old lady lying across the fire guard, dangerously close to the fire, her left shoulder almost touching the top of the hob. Moving swiftly, Pimbo pulled Granny on to the sofa, at the same time feeling the slight scorching of her coloured overall.

"Got it for Christmas!" Granny mumbled. "I get an overall, and a pair of lisle stockings — every Christmas!"

Pimbo smiled down at the old girl. Her fall, with

near disaster, was a long way from her mind, just lisle stockings and a coloured overall. His thoughts went to Italy, shopping for presents, something special for Jenny, two pairs of real silk stockings, and no coupons!

But, in a real young man's style, he'd paid no heed of size, denier or shade. Consequently, a wide-eyed expectant Jenny, received a sized-foot fit only for a midget, a shade of smoky grey, and a thickness which might have brought joy to a maiden aunt plagued with varicose veins!

Granny Bumkins was sitting up, sipping tea, which Jenny had brought in. At that moment, Molly had returned from her college stint. Jenny slipped her a welcome cup of tea, as she anxiously listened to Pimbo's version of the accident.

"Mum's had some near misses, gets black-outs, then falls down. The doctor says as how nothing can be done. It's a good thing you were here — I could do with a break really, but you know what brother's are! The apple of mum's eye when they're kids — but when it comes to doing a stint of care-nursing — well, I suppose men just aren't cut out for it!"

Jenny showed Molly the dyed curtains which were drying outside on the clothes line. The young newly-wed explained how, somehow, she had wanted to see something of her own. Molly patted her on the shoulder. "Why not, gal; by the time I'm home from work, done my bits and pieces, then with mum having me up at 2 a.m. — well, I've lost all zest for making changes, curtains, to me, are just something that either keep out the light — or let it in!"

A knock at the back door revealed, on Molly's opening, two elderly gipsy-looking men, who were proffering lino for sale. "A lovely pattern, ma'am, no dockets, cheap, and long wearing, suitable for kitchen or bedroom, washes well, and will polish until you see your face in it — there, I'm giving it away — fifteen quid! And I'll throw in a coconut door-mat for good luck!"

Molly was slowly closing the door, before the man had finished his sales patter. "No thank you, good day!" she snapped.

Jenny smiled as they returned to the kitchen. She felt that Molly had been a little too curt. Linoleum was hard to come by, even with dockets. A sense of adventure prompted her to feel that building up a home, for two young people, already baptized in the frailties of life — was something they must grasp when the opportunity came —

"I know what you're thinking!" said Molly, suddenly. "That I was too sharp with the men — maybe *you* would have taken a chance on the lino — well, come upstairs with me — I'll show you why I turned the shysters away!"

In her bedroom, Molly pulled away the bed from the side of the wall. On the floor was laid a length of coloured lino, it was of a floral pattern, and at first glance seemed of good quality. Molly pushed back the bed, lifting up a woolly mat, which laid at the side of the bed. Jenny stared, underneath the mat, the lino was bare of all pattern.

Molly laughed cynically. "You see, the pattern was merely printed on a type of cheap cardboard. With no tread under the bed, the pattern remains intact. I was really done — but with no dockets, you've no pull on the crooks. The lino, actually stood up to two days' tread, then the pattern went — I was greedy and paid the price!" sighed Molly.

Jenny had heard many tales of crooked deals — an aftermath of a long war, that had stripped the country of its ability to supply anything other than destructive elements. Now, it was utility clothing, a suit for men at two-pounds-fifty, a costume for women at twenty-two pounds. There was under-counter stuff available for those with money — meat, sausages, liver, bacon — now, was on a par with that which was put out on bird tables in pre-war days!

Through Molly's bedroom window, Jenny could see her newly dyed curtains flapping in the breeze. The golden dye, shining out as autumn splendour left Jenny with a feeling of pride — at least she was improvising! One thing, though — she remembered the old housekeeper in service, who would advise rigidly, 'make sure your curtains have linings — or the sun will burn through them like a dose of acid'!

Molly brought her back to reality. "Let that be a lesson, my girl. Think twice before you think you've got a bargain! The post-war is full of mugs!"

To be on the safe side, Molly called in the doctor to her mother. The GP, finding things a little more strenuous than during the war years; now, it was tummy trouble from Tommies eating different types of food, gave Granny a good looking over. "Just a little bruising on the shoulder — her overall protected her from burns. Not much we can do for her really, syncope attacks may occur anytime, anywhere — just keep her warm, and, of course, a

Over a cup of tea the bargain was sealed.

watchful eye on her!"

Over a cup of tea, Molly confided to Jenny. "Mum's a handful really — but, when *I* was a handful as a baby, she brought me up. It's only fair that I do the same for her. When she goes, bless her, the house will be mine. Maybe, I'll meet a nice fellow, get spliced — who knows?"

Jenny smiled. It would mean yet another move — as Pimbo once joked, "We need a house on wheels!"

CHAPTER 4

More Trouble

Pimbo was digging in well at Tovey Transport. He was mugging up on the Spare Parts Manual. A new part ordered by him, had to be listed by its correct name in the order book. Mechanics tended to use slang terms for various parts; 'half-shafts', 'steering knuckles', and 'king-pin bushes', each had its proper name in the technical manual. This gave Pimbo enhanced status in the eyes of the mechanics, a far cry from his early days, when he was only too pleased to recognize awkward looking gaskets.

Then too, Mr Wilson was proving invaluable towards making Pimbo an efficient store-keeper. A few parts, such as, water-pumps, carburettors and various springs, could be obtained at Murketts Garage on receipt of a Tovey invoice. As in many trades, slovenly staff might settle for a new part, instead of having a go at re-conditioning. "Sometimes!" Mr Wilson would point out, "a water-pump might require just a new gland nut, a matter of a few minutes work by an efficient workman. Instead, unwittingly, by an inexperienced storekeeper, a new, or reconditioned part would be purchased, costing the firm needless expense!"

Next morning, Mr Ransome came in from the Regent Street office. "We're losing stock, I've checked Murkett Bro's. invoices over the last six months, we find that the amount of carburettors and other spares purchased just don't tally with the job sheet — I know it's not your fault, but it's time something were done!"

After Mr Ransome had departed, Pimbo took the matter up with the elderly mechanic. Mr Wilson shrugged amicably, "You know, boy, you can put a lot of this down to the war. A lot of lads got so used to 'winning' things that it came second nature. In Egypt, when a British soldier boarded a tram, he didn't pay — just said 'Churchill will pay'. It gets in the blood, comes too easy – !"

"But, what's the answer, I don't want to get anyone the sack?" pleaded Pimbo.

"Get all your stock cards up to date. Then on Saturday and Sunday, any stock taken, and not listed on a job sheet — would be 'knocked off'; you won't find the culprit, but at least you'll know who were on duty over the weekend. Should it be just one man on a job-sheet — then he's your man!"

During the break, Pimbo gave it deep thought. He mused on the fact that jobs weren't easy to get. Most of the mechanics he liked, one of the drivers, George, went to school with him. Then, too, maybe someone *outside* the work staff could be breaking in over the weekend? He decided to look at it from a new angle, so told the men.

"From this weekend, a check will be made on everything going from the stores. Maybe, some of you are forgetting to log them on your job sheets, but, it seems there is a discrepancy, between what goes out and what remains on the stock cards! Furthermore, it will put you all in the clear, you see, Mr Ransome's been getting a little worried of late!"

On the way home, Pimbo realised how much easier it would have been had Tovey allowed him to come in on weekends. A bit of overtime would have been very acceptable, he supposed the firm had left open the door for a little fiddling — 'Perks', 'Winnings', was a new post-war disease. Pimbo smiled as he remembered his being in charge of a gun-site at Oakington. It was a bitter winter, with his men shivering in an old bell tent.

A nearby building site, with plenty of half-finished sections of wood partitions, had made a nice comfortable shed. A brand new stove was purloined, giving the lads home-from-home comforts. A cement mixer, borrowed over the weekend, ended up with a cracked cylinder (the lads forgot to replenish with water, which the workmen had emptied against the frost). All, really, stolen, borrowed, won, purloined — but without a hint of conscience!

Jenny smiled at her young husband's story of the day's events. She, too, realised that it might take a few years to rid the system of its 'winning ways'. You can't let young blood run loose over foreign lands, see the greed caused through useless wars — the upper crust, no doubt, were doing their 'bit' in another way — but it all meant the same thing really!

Jenny filled in Pimbo with her day's doings. A trip to the Guildhall in order to boost up her chances of getting a Council house. The nearest she had got to enlightenment, was the fact that a vacancy might crop up in one of the Nissen huts on Donkey's Common. Jenny had just missed a little house in Caroline Place; a close friend sent a note that morning, but having called on the way to the Housing Office, Jenny learned of its letting.

On the way back, she stopped in Burleigh Street. Cyril Lord, the carpet tycoon, was opening up a new store. She stared in awe at the lovely display. The amount of dockets required was breathtaking, but the patterns, so far removed from austerity, dazzled her eyes. "How'd you like that lot in your front room, gal?" a neighbour was saying to another. "Your o'le man would have to alter, eh, flicking his Woodbine ash on to the carpet, you'd be after him, eh, Elsie?"

Jenny smiled at the women's humour, the good old British way of getting over difficulties. She noticed the large new store of John Blundell's; lovely goods to attract the young wives of a post-war era, were creeping back into circulation, there, a little bit of colour, here, a new design. Kleen-ezie, and Better-wear, both brush manufacturers on a par with Fuller's of America, were offering openings to young men, with a salary as limitless as the sky. Coloured floor mops, special polishes, brushes for every purpose, made with an eye on practical design, door-to-door selling, but certainly a new innovation to brighten the post-war blues!

After seeing off Pimbo to work, plus making sure his daily dose of cod-liver-oil-and-malt, had been taken, Jenny moved into the kitchen where

Granny Bumkins was partaking of a drink of
Bovril. Somehow the old lady did not seem as well
as usual. She seemed loathe to move, just laying
back and breathing heavily. Usually, she might
have treated Jenny to some humorous aside,
taking her back many years, when the old lady was
a seamstress for Suttle's. 'Lap seaming', and
'double-binds' took up a great part of her vocabul-
ary.

Molly would confirm much of her gabbled
statements. That mum was once in charge of a
team of seamstresses, worked very hard, and long
hours for very little pay, but was dedicated in her
work. In her declining years, Granny's thoughts
went back to her working days — hardly ever
mentioning other parts of her life. Suttle's was a
large store in Fitzroy Street, with a works department in City Road where sewing machines rattled
away from dawn 'til dusk.

As soon as Molly arrived from work, after a quick
look at her mother, she called in the doctor, who
moved Granny into hospital with suspected
broncho-pneumonia and other old-age complica-
tions.

Over a cup of tea, Molly confided to Jenny of her
fears that one day her mother would have just one
illness 'too many'. That's one thing, Jenny, should
anything happen to Mum, I won't turn you out — in
fact, you can have the front room, and I'll be happy
with the kitchen and the room you now use!" Jenny
thanked her profusely. It would give her a chance
to save for the day when a Council house would be
theirs.

"I take it the house will be yours on the strength

that you have looked after your Mum?" queried
Jenny. "Has your Mum signed anything to this
effect — I did hear of a case where the eldest son
took the house despite his sister's looking after the
mother for several years?"

Molly looked thoughtful. "It's a point, Jenny. But
Mum's always said that the house will be mine on
her death. She's never showed me papers to that
effect — but on the other hand, my brother has
never questioned my stay in the house — surely he
won't expect me to move out if Mum dies?"

Jenny could hear Pimbo putting away his cycle
in the garden shed. When he entered the kitchen,
his young wife presented him with the proverbial
cup of tea, and filled him in concerning Granny's
departure to hospital. "Right — you two! Off to the
pictures, an evening out for the pair of you. Molly
hasn't had a break for months — it'll give me time
to swot up on our new spares manual!"

On their way to the Kinema, the two friends
swapped feelings.

"I sometimes wonder where it will all end!" Molly
was saying. "I have a fancy man of my own, you
know! He keeps asking me to make a break —
marry him, while I'm still — well, you know, young
enough to make it a real marriage. But I can't leave
Mum, my brother can't have her — so my hands are
tied!"

Jenny nodded. Funny, she was thinking how it
was that everyone seemed bogged down by domestic and social problems. During her ATS days, she
had presumed that getting married would ultimately bring all the happiness that a young girl
dreamed of. Not that she wasn't happy with Pimbo,

oh, no — but that little dream house seemed *so* far away!

Molly broke her thoughts. As they moved into Mill Road, she pointed out the little railway cottages, which had been bombed during the war. "They tell me that the Council are doing them up — letting them to problem families — strikes me, aren't we all problem families? Still, I wouldn't fancy one, too near the railway lines, must shake the ceilings down, more like the new song about the train lines running through the centre of the house!"

Reaching the Playhouse, Molly treated Jenny to an ice-cream, and pop-corns. The film 'The Best Years of Our Lives' was a new release, depicting the aftermath of a long war, with the home-coming of an armless war veteran, comparing his lot with that of his two pals, sound in mind and limb, but less morally stable, with their subsequent drinking and womanising, making them more emotionally crippled than their pal with a genuine physical disability.

When Molly and Jenny arrived home from their evening off, they found Pimbo at the door to greet them. "Granny's had a slight stroke, your brother came round — says as not to worry, she's comfortable, and there's nothing you can do at this hour — he'll meet you at the hospital in the morning!"

Over a cup of tea, the trio sat wondering as to the outcome. Molly held back a tear as she went over the list of sisters whom she would have to contact should Mum die. Jenny was thinking of an old lady she knew, whose daughters, with the exception of

one, Mary, had visited their mother regularly.
Ironically, when she did eventually arrive, Mary
was treated as a 'Prodigal daughter' –

Alone in their room, Pimbo and Jenny tried hard
to cheer themselves up. They were young, happily
married, yet, somehow seemed caught up in a
series of mishaps and trauma. They wondered how
many back-room couples there were in Cambridge
in a like situation. The local paper was riddled with
'adverts', wants for bed-sitters, furnished accommodation. A tribunal had been set up to guard
against overcharging for inadequate accommodation. Jenny remembered one such case. A Mrs
Shorter of Tenison Avenue had her fees knocked
down from £23 to fifteen pounds, apparently the
room she had on offer boasted as furniture — just
one humped-back sofa!

Pimbo had pointed out an 'advert' for caretakers
at the Leys School. The school offered a three-
roomed flat, with a wage to bolster up the vacancy's
attraction. Jenny gave Pimbo a wry smile.

"In-service jobs, usually, are poorly paid. Once
your name comes off the Council list, you stand
very little chance of getting back on. Besides, Molly
has told me that we can stay here when Granny
dies, why the worry about our moving out?"

Pimbo moved across to his young wife, then
placed his arm on her shoulder. "I don't want to
worry you, Jenny. But I said nothing in front of
Molly, you see, when her brother called, we had a
chat. It's cut and dried that her brother will get the
house when his mother dies. True, there is no legal
document, but the eldest son gets priority, that's
the present law!"

Jenny stared in awe, at Cyril Lord's lovely carpet display.

Jenny's lips tightened. "If that's the case, well, I'm going to tell Molly — all these years she's been sacrificing — for what? Surely, you don't expect her to take this lying down, I'll — I'll go with her to a solicitor, we'll find out for sure – !"

"I knew that you'd take it like this!" put in Pimbo quietly. "Trust my girl for that; I suppose it's a case of blood being thicker than water, his son's getting married, when Granny dies, they'll move in here.

That's why I've been looking for jobs with accommodation — you see, Jenny, we must look ahead!"

Jenny snorted. "Granny isn't dead yet. In the meantime, me and Molly will take ourselves down to a solicitor in the morning, we'll thrash it out one way or another. And another thing, did that brother of hers say exactly where he intends sending Molly — will she get a roof over *her* head?"

Pimbo and Jenny stared at each other. Through a harsh long war they had moved from barrack room to slit-trench, from tent to fox-hole, from good rations to bad, from desert to sergeants quarters. Now, they were still at it — on the move!

Smilingly, they hugged each other. "As long as we're together — what's it matter!" whispered Pimbo in Jenny's ear!

CHAPTER 5

A New Pre-fab,
and a New Baby!

In the middle of Pimbo's 'missing stores' sojourn,
and Jenny's trauma with the ensuing death of
Granny Bumkins, came a breakthrough for the
young couple. Jenny was expecting a baby; and in
view of the mounting points which had placed her
well up in the housing list — a new pre-fab on the
Church End estate at Cherryhinton was their's for
the taking!

With excitement and anticipation, Jenny
mounted the stairs on her way to the Housing
Department of the Guildhall. She smiled as she
noticed the tea-trolleys being taken into various
little side-rooms. Then, too, she remembered the
little chit-chat of queue gossip, it seemed, that to
the working fraternity of Cambridge, a visit to the
Guildhall was one fraught with verbal battles, and
a fight for one's principle!

Jenny was ushered into a small room, where a
frosty-faced, spinster-type middle aged lady faced
her over a small counter, with glass sections at
either side. "Oh, you're Mrs Unwin, I believe?
Called for your key and rent book, I presume? Now,

my dear, you do realise how important it is that you pay your rent regularly, keep your house and garden neat and tidy — the Council expect the best from their tenants — you know!"

Jenny kept cool as she waited until both rent-book and key were safely clutched in her waiting palms; then calmly, she stared into the woman's face. "I'm expecting a baby, I may not be able to attend early morning roll-calls, it's likely, too, that I might miss a few parades and route-marches — but, a chit from the M.O., you know - 'excused boots' or 'Fire Picket' may override my shortcomings!"

Jenny, without waiting for a further response from the good lady, did a smart turn-about as she left the room!

Pimbo was almost delirious with excitement as Jenny told him the good news. With the death of Granny Bumkins, the problems of their stay at Hooper Street would now be solved. Jenny's visit to a solicitor with Molly confirmed that the house was definitely her brother's, although, a new law, safeguarding sacrificial daughters undergoing a similar fate to that of poor Molly, was being put into effect!

It was a grand morning when Peak's removal van turned up in Hooper Street. Pimbo and Jenny's pitifully few belonging were soon loaded into the awaiting van. Molly was crying as she bade the happy couple goodbye. "I'll be moving into a house a few doors away from Noah Northfield — come round and see me, won't you? At least I've finished with a roof over my head!"

Jenny and Pimbo's new address was 180 Church

End, Cherryhinton. The whole estate, with its glistening white prefabricated bungalows, reminded Jenny of the many American films which depicted an open-plan array of neat homes with lovely gardens, no fences or boundary hedges. A complete sense of freedom permeated through the whole estate, as though the Government was saying, "Here it is at long last, an estate fit for heroes to live — go to it — bring up your children, and start a new community!"

The prefab consisted of a lounge, hall, kitchen, bathroom, and two bedrooms. To Jenny's delight, in the kitchen was a complete unit running along one side: Electric cooker, refrigerator, sink, and working top. It seemed a luxury beyond her wildest dreams, Jenny smiled as she thought of Noah's tiny kitchen, with its old-fashioned gas stove, and Noah's persistent habit of boiling up old dish-cloths in a saucepan, which did service almost twenty-four hours a day.

Almost opposite her front entrance, Jenny could see the lovely old Church, standing amidst the trees; as though keeping an eye on the young mothers-to-be.

Pimbo, in the quiet of the evening, when their few sticks of furniture had been placed into position, sprung yet another surprise on Jenny.

"I'm leaving Tovey's. I've got a job as a milkman with Stetchworth Dairies. The money's better, I get a commission, I can be finished by dinner-time, it'll leave me more time for the garden, and to be with you when the baby comes!"

His young wife, too overcome with recent events, offered no resistance to Pimbo's plan. Over a cup of tea, Pimbo pushed home further his newly-found initiative. "When the baby starts coming, don't panic. Leave it to me, there's a phone box on the corner, I'll have the ambulance here in no time!"

Pimbos' milk round consisted of Tenison Road, Lynewode Road, Glisson Road, Tenison Avenue, finishing up in St Barnabas Road. An electric trolley in lieu of a horse-driven cart made it much easier for the roundsman to leave his float unattended. On the finishing of his round, Pimbo was required to leave his trolley on electric charge.

Pimbo's first morning went reasonably well. A lady in Tenison Road, almost opposite the Salvation Army Citadel, had ready a steaming hot cup of tea as the new roundsman came to her door. Her husband, a captain in the S.A., recently had undergone a slight stroke, despite this handicap, he gave Pimbo a welcome smile. Many and varied were the customers on the round. A dear little lady, Mrs Honeyman, her husband an eighteen-stone retired Parson, living in St Barnabas Road, often used Pimbo to help lift her stroke-ridden spouse from the floor back to his bed. At the top of the same road, lived Mr Symonds, the Labour councillor, who won over the Cambridge seat against odds.

Milk rationing was still in force, this made it very difficult for Pimbo to decide where an extra half-pint could be fairly distributed. Customers, such as Fred Day's classy hairdressing salon, were ever trying to eke out milk for their 'coffee under the drier' clientele. They paid handsomely for such small mercies, happy in the fact that all was above board.

Then, too, pensioners, living alone, tied down to

just half-pint a day, gave Pimbo many a heart-ache, when they left out a note pleading for anything extra, as they had 'company coming'!

On returning home from his first day, Pimbo, anxious to tell Jenny about his adventures, found a weeping Molly, who, although pleased with her new little home, was finding the transition from Hooper Street very emotional.

Jenny was doing her best to console her. "You've done your best for your mum. You can't buy a clear conscience, you nursed her until the end — now start living yourself! Your brother gets the house it's true, but he is within the law, your mother signed nothing — so she left things wide open; life is full of such happenings — tell you what — I want you to be God Mother to my baby when it comes! You can relive your life through a little creature coming into a world which you found wanting — now dry those eyes and start afresh!"

"That's right!" said Pimbo, coming in on Jenny's statement. "Look at me, Troop Sergeant turned milkman, I visit homes, have notes left me, make decisions on vital points, as to who might be lucky in getting an extra drop of milk in their tea — there, *now* you're on your own, you can look out for a partner, it's all happening for you, really Molly!"

On Molly's departure Jenny confided to Pimbo that her visit to Mill Road Maternity Unit confirmed that the baby was due any day now, and that she must take things easy. The rest of the day the happy couple spent in preparing the baby clothes, checking up the cot equipment, and making sure that Pimbo knew off by heart the number to dial for the ambulance.

They both laughed as they surveyed the bottles of orange juice, the large tin of cod-liver-oil and malt, and the national dried milk powder, which could be used as a supplementary food for breast-fed babies. Then, too, Jenny had taken religiously bottle after bottle of 'iron' tablets. "I want us to have a bonny baby, the Government has given us a good start in in bringing up baby — we mustn't let it down!" she'd say. Pimbo went along with all that — and more! He wondered whether he might have been spared the horrors of T.B. had those facilities been available. Even Jenny, through rickets as a child, had paid the penalty of those poverty stricken days — now, thank goodness, it was all in reach of everyone, poverty or not!

A chemist in Regent Street loaned out baby scales at a low monthly rental; the newly-weds had taken full advantage of this splendid scheme.

During the night, Jenny suddenly became restless, those 'special' pains had begun. Pimbo, in a deep slumber, woke suddenly as he half-heard Jenny gasp out, "It's coming, quickly Pimbo!"

"Don't panic! Leave it to me!" With those comforting words, the young father-to-be promptly dived into the wardrobe. After a flaying of arms, a rattle of the closet handle, Pimbo realised that he was indeed far from displaying the coolness hitherto advised.

Jenny realigned her dutiful husband in the right direction, and although clad only in pyjamas on a cold winter night, Pimbo made his way to the 'phone box, an act which ultimately saw Jenny on her way to the Maternity Hospital on Mill Road.

Pimbo, as his round evolved around the maternity hospital, decided to carry on working, then at regular intervals, to pop in to see how things were going on. Although not telling Jenny, Pimbo discovered that he was one of the unfortunate husbands who 'carry' their wives' pregnancy, sickness, back-ache, and similar ailments had each assailed the anxious father-to-be!

At 6.30 a.m., before the commencement of his milk round, Pimbo nervously appeared at the nurses station. A group of nurses, about to hand over from their night stint, stared unbelievably at the white-faced young man. "Your wife is still in labour, we think it's in an awkward position — we can't be sure, you must come back again!" blurted out the senior nurse; then, after peering again at Pimbo, she ordered, "Take this young fellow down to the kitchen, get him a good breakfast — he looks in worse shape than his dear wife!"

With his round half-completed, Pimbo once again called at the hospital for further information. "We're sending your wife to Addenbrookes, the baby is in the breech-position, it will be a Caesarean birth. Mr Lloyd will be in charge — everything will be fine!" the young Sister consoled, as Pimbo was allowed a moment or two with Jenny,

Looking pale, Jenny smiled up bravely. "The nurses told me you'd called, and how ill you looked. Ossie Lloyd's a good man, now don't worry, and mind you eat well – !" Before she could say more, Jenny was whisked away, leaving a handful of nurses to console a worried Pimbo.

Phoning several times after work, at last he received the message he was waiting for — it was a girl! Seven pounds — and he could go up to

Addenbrooke's to see his first born!

Mounting the stairs, Pimbo wondered what the baby would look like. Was it OK? No deformity? Would they be good parents, could they manage money-wise? He'd try for a part-time job, the extra money would buy the things a baby must have. Then too, he must take over more responsibility, he remembered in the desert how he'd rapped out orders, a lone Corporal, last out of the tent, stared at Pimbo, who was about to reprimand him, "I've had a letter from home, one of my kids is ill — when you're married, with two kids, you'll understand, Sarg!"

Jenny was looking radiant. Her dark hair, falling over a white flowered nightdress, contrasted beautifully with the beshawled little bundle of charm, which lay cuddled in her arms. Almost afraid to hold her, lest he might clumsily do damage, Pimbo peered down at Christine Anne Unwin, a dark-eyed little beauty if ever there was one!

Jenny looked up, smilingly, "It was worth it! Isn't she lovely?"

Noises from the kitchen, cries from other babies, the dedicated manner of the young nurses. The waiting fathers, not yet told the 'good news'. A lovely smell of baby lotions, powders, and all the paraphanalia of bringing up baby, assailed his nostrils. Then, too, the way some of the nurses stared at him, as though, indeed, he had achieved some remarkable feat. "Well!" said Jenny, suddenly, "Aren't you going to kiss me, you stand there like a creature from outer space?"

With baby Christine, after a feed, safely back in

Pimbo peered down at his new baby.

the nursery, Jenny leaned forward. "I had a bad time. Mr Lloyd was marvellous — but we're lucky — " Jenny pointed to an empty bed. "This poor lady had high blood pressure, she was forty, tried for five years to have a baby. Her husband, from outside Cambridge, was told that at last he had a son, by the time he reached Addenbrookes, the wife had died — but the baby boy was fine — just like a story-book — but true!" finished Jenny. "I shall be out on Friday, now I want you to bring my clothes with you next visit. I'll want to look like a real mother, so make sure you bring the right ones, you'll find them already packed inside the wardrobe!" as she finished, Jenny was laughing.

"What's the joke?" queried Pimbo.

"Yesterday, a young husband caused a real riot in the ward. Instead of collecting his wife's clothes from her clean locker, he, in panic, fished them out of the dirty laundry basket. The wife, at first, was furious, then saw the funny side of it, the whole ward was in uproar!"

"Then again!" went on Jenny, "after her husband had gone, the wife was checking the bundle he'd left. 'By heck!' she was telling the entire ward, 'where the hell did he get the stuff he's brought in! I've not worn them for years, I'd forgotten I had them — I'll never understand men!'."

"But you understand me?" asked Pimbo cheekily.

Jenny leaned forward and kissed him. "I mustn't forget to give my milk tokens to my milkman, Christine is another mouth to feed, you know!"

There was no doubt about it. Milkmen did a good job, mused Pimbo as he made his way home!

THE PRE-FAB

There was a pre-fab, in old Church End,
In Cherryhinton, where, once we dwelt.
In the years to come, we wish to blend;
Our thoughts, and how we felt!

Jenny was young, and I was young,
And we dreamed, and had no care.
Much dearer, and better, than life has been;
Were the dreams that came to us there!

There were Penny and Chas, beginning as we,
The Beilby's, Johnny Coward and wife.
Hoping, and dreaming, that the world might be,
Bereft of sadness and strife.

When we are weary of this present day,
Of the turmoil and its pain.
We'll dream of the pre-fab that beaconed our way;
And long to be there again!

Fred Unwin

CHAPTER 6

Married Life's Problems Set In

Jenny was finding the new addition to the family a great asset in finding new friends. Mrs Beilby, next door, wife of a postman, popped in now and again. "Reminds me of my first, I had a bad time like you, but my mother-in-law drove me mad. Insisted that I put the baby in a chest binder — I had to bring in the midwife to put her right!"

Penny Orders, living a few doors up, proved a staunch neighbour. Although far from well off, with a sick husband, Penny was ever cheery and having been reared from a family of seven, had stacks of good advice to offer. Her mother, who often visited, was a marvellous character, very fit for her years, could sew, grow vegetables, cook like a chef, and turn her hand to almost anything.

Baby Christine was getting on splendidly. Very good at night; making it ludicrous that Pimbo, having brought a new alarm clock, setting it at 2 a.m. — "In case baby awoke, and we didn't hear her!" Pimbo found it hard to live down with his new neighbours.

"Money's tight!" Jenny was saying one evening. "Any chance of your earning more, I mean, as you once said — getting a part-time job, gardening or something?"

"I know what you mean, I saw the electricity bill, I often wonder if the 'frig runs away with it, someone told me at times it gets stuck — puts up the bill that way!" Pimbo sighed, as he looked through the window at his little vegetable patch. It would save money once they had been put on the dinner table, but — !

"A lady in Lynewode Road wants me to cut her lawns, looks as though it might be a regular stint, I'll give it a go this afternoon — keep your fingers crossed!"

Jenny smiled as she saw her young spouse pedal away. She hadn't told him everything, but by mid-week her purse was practically empty.

Pimbo's potential employer lived almost opposite the Lydemonds; Mr Lydemond, being a teacher at the Perse School in Bateman Street. The good lady, whose lawn needed cutting, met her would-be-gardener at the back door. "I'd like you to give the mower a good haul-over before you start, my old gardener seems to have neglected it somewhat, here's the key to the shed!"

Pimbo smiled as he viewed the shiny new padlock, which had been thrust through a staple so old and rusty, that it was much easier to pull out the staple and leave the padlock intact. The shed was in little better condition than the staple, but, somehow he managed to extricate the mower from the shed without the building collapsing around his ears.

The mower was of a vintage type, hard to push, with its rotating blades as blunt as a fish-knife.

Viewing the expansive lawn, Pimbo reckoned it would take hours to cut, especially as many of the flowering plants hung over the edges of the lawn. Taking an old rasping file from the shed, he ran the serations over the mower's rotor blades; to his chagrin the old file actually shed its rough edges, making the task of sharpening the mower impossible.

A voice from the back door halted his activities. "Like a cup of tea, my man. Come along then, it'll soon get cold!" Wiping the mud from his boots, Pimbo entered the small kitchen.

"My sister's just gone away for a few weeks, I'm Miss Doris Forbes, you've never met me before; Alice is the dominant member of the house — leaves the administration to me, you know!" The speaker, a thin elegant lady, placed the cup of tea before Pimbo.

"But the mower, the shed, it all seems so old, I can't do justice to the money you'd have to pay me — but why — ?"

Miss Forbes smiled wryly. "My sister was born in South Africa, I came to school in England, she stayed behind with Daddy, he was an engineer, road and bridge building, bossed it over three-hundred employees!"

"But your mother?" queried Pimbo.

"Mummy couldn't settle, she had no time for the internal politics, so after twenty years, she came back to England bringing my sister Alice with her. Daddy died a year later, killed in an engineering accident. I'm afraid the mower, the lawn, are just gimmicks, an excuse for me to have a chat with someone — you must be the sixth milkman to have a go at that mower — !"

"And your mother" put in Pimbo.

"Married again, left the house to the both of us, lives in Devon, comes down to see us twice a year, insists that the old gardener tidies up now and again to keep it within the bounds of decency!"

Pimbo was about to move away from the table, as Doris, taking a ten-shilling note from her purse, proffered it to a surprised young man.

"Your relief roundsman told me about your new baby, I'm sorry about everything, but please take it, you've come a long a way on that cycle of yours!"

Pimbo was thinking what ten shillings could buy; a joint for the week-end, two weeks supply of milk at two pints per day, half the week's rent, 2 cwts of coal, an excursion trip to Hunstanton, or a lovely little dress for Christine!

He took the ten shilling note, placing it in his back pocket. "It's against my principle, really, my old dad would turn in his grave — but you're so kind, you would be hurt if I refuse — should you ever get a new lawn mower, contact me — 'have mower — will travel', you might say, and thanks for the tea!"

As he neared the junction at the church near his home, Pimbo noticed a lot of activity going on in and around the estate vicinity. Jenny met him at the bottom of the path, "It's a missing child, a little boy from Mill Street off Mill Road, left home between 1 p.m. and 2 p.m., he's riding a fairy cycle, his mum's frantic, he's only four!"

Realising that his journey home had embraced the tin-walk running alongside the cement works in Coldham's Lane and that a large area comprised of deep quarries and water-logged, dangerous sand pits, which might attract a young child, skirted much of the territory that the little boy might have travelled along.

Jenny broke his thoughts. "The boy was reported as being seen in the neighbourhood, he must be around here somewhere!"

A little band of anxious neighbours had gathered, discussing what to do. Pimbo, with memories of his Army days, took over; splitting them up into separate areas in which to search. With three others, he decided to search around the cement-works danger spots before darkness actually set in.

Several hours of diligent searching had brought nothing. Every yard had been covered, making it impossible for the boy to have broken through the cordon of anxious searchers. Pimbo decided to try another locality making his way back with the three helpers to their starting point. A sudden shout, a scurrying of fleeting figures emerging from the darkening shadows and a soul-searching cry of 'we've found him!' lifted their sinking spirits.

A woman was pointing excitedly into a large hedge, a hedge which Pimbo and his followers had passed by on their way to the cement works. "It was my dog, led me straight into the hedge, fast asleep he was, still on his little tricycle, thank God we found him — they say tonight would have been a very hard frost!"

"I've had quite a day!" Pimbo told Jenny, as he sat back with a hot drink, after the goings and comings of news reporters, and excited Church End neighbours. Slipping the ten shilling note into her hand, the young husband smiled as Jenny, placing it between the rent book, then looked up. "We pay the rent once a fortnight, it's the Electricity Board this week. Oh, by the way, I took Christine down with me to the Electricity Board this afternoon, I queried the bill, told them about the 'frig. The man said they had had a similar problem on this estate, reckons I'm eligible for a rebate, a little turn-table in the circuit gets stuck, and can double the bill — they're sending a chap down to check up!"

Pimbo had missed seeing Christine before her bedtime. A little game in the bath, a cuddle on the lap, or a romp on the floor, now she lay, fast asleep, hands clutching teddy. "What's she been up to today?" queried Pimbo.

"Same as you — gardening!" laughed back Jenny, taking her husband to the window looking out onto the back lawn. Pimbo stared in dismay at the sorry sight of four geraniums, placed strategically at each corner of the lawn, standing headless, bereft of all their crowning glory.

"Somehow, she managed to pick up the scissors, before you could say John the Baptist, off came their heads! I was more cross at my negligence than the loss of the geraniums!" smiled Jenny.

Pimbo nodded in assent. His gaze moved across to his next door neighbour's garden. A nice friendly little man, a civil-servant, who did all his gardening text-book style. For days, all you could see was the top of his head as he double-dug the little patch, then to repeat the performance on the way back.

Came the smoothing of the lumpy soil, then the setting of plants, beetroot, beans, cabbage, and lettuce. One day, leaning over the fence in conversation with him, Pimbo noticed that every-one of his neighbour's plants were in the process of wilting. Calling over an expert gardener a few doors away, the civil-servant was told that slugs had burrowed their way to the roots of the plants — and worse still, Pimbo's garden had been treated by the slugs as a kind of no-man's land — free of all molestation!

As a kind of condolence, Pimbo had given over some of his spare crop, tomatoes, celery and potatoes. The little man was most grateful, promis-ing to look up a few more text-books. Pimbo was tempted to offer Christine, complete with scissors, as a means of defeating the slug menace in a positive way!

To Jenny's surprise, a cry from Christine's room told her that the toddler was awake. Pimbo was in like a shot, bringing out a red-cheeked infant, who, as Jenny pointed out, "She must be cutting her teeth".

Glancing at the clock, Pimbo noticed it was almost nine-o'clock. Never before had he known Christine to be up so late. "Rub this on her gums!" said Jenny. "It'll soothe her, and by the time we're ready for bed, perhaps she'll drop off!"

A sudden knock at the door, let in a woman who, to Jenny's surprise, turned out to be the lady from the Guildhall, whom she'd crossed swords with over the key and rent book.

Blushing a deep red, the woman accepted a chair proffered by Pimbo. "I'm Miss Webb, sorry to be rather late, but I've had a busy evening, the missing boy caused a lot of people to be out. I'm from the Young Wives Fellowship, I wonder whether you'd like to join our group?"

Jenny stared across at Pimbo, as though to gain support in one way or another. Christine, apparently finding the gum solvent a great help against teething, was by now her usual bright and bouncing self, laughing and gurgling away.

Jenny was not quite sure whether Miss Webb had recognised her as the young wife who had shown very little fellowship over the key and rent book fiasco!

"Well, I'm afraid at the moment my time is taken up with bringing up baby; my husband, too, is taking on part-time jobs, I can't guarantee any specified time – what sort of programme have you in mind?"

Miss Webb fidgetted in her chair, and after looking around the room, taking a long hard look at Christine, who was still showing bags of life, straightened up, displaying for the first time her 'Guildhall' look.

"Well, we aim to help young wives to bring up their youngsters in a healthy way. I mean — er — take tonight, it's almost nine-thirty, I see your child is not yet asleep — we advise on breast-feeding and when to wean, although the baby clinics give a similar service, we don't intend to over-lap, but some mothers do slip through the net — you know!"

Jenny, giving Pimbo a cheeky wink picked up the bottle of gum-soothing lotion. "My child is teething, she normally would, at this time, be tucked up in bed. By the way, Miss Webb, have you ever had any children, or do you go rigidly by the text-book — we have a neighbour next door, who goes by the text-book, but he's sensible enough to know that it doesn't allow for the laws of nature not to creep in!"

The 'Guildhall' lady stood up quickly. "I think now, on after-thought, that we *have* met before. I don't want to waste your time further, it seems that you go through life looking for confrontations — good-night!"

"Good-night, mind the step as you go out, and please remember that it takes two people to confront each other, and *you* always make sure that you're the first on the scene!" Jenny retorted.

Once again on their own, with Christine at last asleep, the young couple stared at each other. Pimbo broke the silence.

"Well, dear, I've never had such a day as this, if this is married life — we'll be old before we're young!"

Jenny, putting on the kettle for the last drink of the evening, smiled back. "I think we've learnt a good deal. Miss Webb isn't really a true model of bureaucracy, it takes all to make a world. I suppose there are some mothers that need a Miss Webb behind them — !"

"As long as she stays *behind* us, it'll suit me. But seriously, though, our poor old great-grandmothers must have found it tough going, I mean, none of this kind of Webb lark for them, what with chest binding and poor hygiene — !"

"They managed, on far less than we do!" put in Jenny. "You take some of the old photographs, lovely white pinafores for the girls, and warm jersey's for the boys!"

Have mower — will travel!

Pimbo was thinking of Miss Doris and the old mower, he supposed that the dear lady might be much happier were she to take on part of their life, Miss Webb, warts and all! There would be little need for gimmicks to start off a friendship —

He smiled at Jenny's reference to the text-book logic of Miss Webb. In the Army, a text-book manual was issued with every weapon. Pimbo remembered how peppered each manual was with amendments. He reckoned that should a manual on married life ever be published, its sequel need be no more than a complete book of amendments.

But Jenny was now ready for bed; baby Christine was sleeping soundly as he peeped into her cot. Somehow the young couple would get by under their own steam — it was all part of married life!

CHAPTER 7

A False Accusation

Pimbo was getting on well with his milk round. News of his becoming a daddy brought lots of friendly banter; one dear old lady presented him with a hand-knitted matinee jacket, big enough to fit only the smallest of dolls. "I've kept it in mothballs — in case — you know? But I never married!"

The round was full of characters; Mr Challis of Tenison Road, who could always be relied upon for a crisp letter to the local editor on any subject. Mr Green, a very learned solicitor, who was ever taking up the cudjel on someone's behalf. At the bottom of Glisson Road, Mr Bowles, the saddler and son, busily stitching away at equestrian equipment. Mr Rex Freeman lived with his mother at the bottom end of the long road. Rex was a multi-talented young man, music, drama, singing, all aided and abetted by his enthusiastic mum.

But suddenly, things started going wrong! "You're short on your takings!" Mr Hall, the dairy manager confronted him with. Pimbo wasn't unduly worried, it was easy to miss out on an extra pint 'called' after, in the middle of the street. "I'll go through my book with a tooth-comb, I'll find it somewhere!" Pimbo confided.

The dairy manager was a very nice man, an old cockney, coming down from London, to take a job which gave him accommodation and a reasonable living. Pimbo knew there was no personal vendetta in the accusation — just a matter of keeping the books straight.

Other members of the staff were equally easy to get on with. Mr Tuppling, an amazing man, well on in years, but he threw milk-churns about as though they were lightweights. He worked as hard as any man Pimbo had known, and above all, was ever cheery and ready for a chat.

Reg Childerley, a Coton stalwart, with six brothers, almost making a football team on their own. Reg operated the bottling machine, which was in itself a work of art. Pimbo usually kept his fingers crossed when coming in to pick up his second supply of milk. The bottling machine at times was very tempermental! With Albert Norman, the yard foreman, a very astute, hard-working man, who knew all the rounds almost off by heart, a good happy staff kept things ticking over very well.

To offset the cash shortage, Pimbo popped any 'tips' or extras back into the bag. But, somehow, it didn't work out; each week-end, Mr Hall, with his face growing longer, told of a further shortage.

Jenny was taking the affair very badly, suggesting that Pimbo should give in his notice, rather than be accepted as a thief. For hours at night, just before collection on Friday, Jenny would help

Pimbo to go through his book, there seemed
nothing to merit a shortage, every item was
checked, the money that Pimbo had handed in
since the so-called shortage, tallied exactly with
the outgoing dairy produce — apart from the few
tips thrown in as a security against shortage.

"If I'm short this week-end, I'll hand in my
notice!" declared Pimbo, after a strenuous session
of check and double check!" Jenny gave him an
extra kiss as he left the house on his week-end
delivery and collection. "Don't worry, I my old
boy's a good 'un, I didn't marry you for nothing!"

But, it happened for the final time! The dairy
manager met him on the Sunday morning, "I'm
sorry, boy, but you'll have to do something, the
shortage is getting out of proportion — you're a
popular roundsman, but there's something going
wrong somewhere, are you in trouble at home,
any debts, or — ?"

Pimbo couldn't believe his ears, he was actually
being accused of theft. "You can take my notice,
Mr Hall; one day you'll find out, maybe you've got
a phoney calculator — but I wouldn't touch a
penny of your money, in fact I've been throwing
back my 'tips' for weeks!"

The next two days were back holidays for
Pimbo, as the days were owing him from a
roundsman being off sick, and Pimbo helping out
with his round.

Albert Norman, would be doing Pimbo's round,
he would usually pop in for a cup of tea, and to
hand over Pimbo's rounds book. Jenny was looking through her sitting room window as Albert
approached the house. To her surprise, the relief-

roundsman spotted her at the window, raising his hand he then pushed up two fingers in a gesture of a victory salute.

Letting him in, Jenny, wondering what it was all about, could hardly wait for his reply. "You're in a good mood, what's the victory sign for?" she asked excitedly.

"Where's Pimbo?" asked Albert.

Jenny's face dropped a little. "He's out looking for a new job. The shortages have got him down, we've checked and checked, Pimbo's cash has always been on the dot!"

"I've found the answer to it, there's no shortage at all, in fact, your husband's takings show a surplus — it was a terrible blunder by the accounts clerk, it had crept up insidiously for weeks and weeks — but, by pure chance — I found out this morning!"

Albert explained over a cup of tea, the whole story. The little dairy-shop had been managed by a Miss Rose, who, on retirement, was living in Tenison Road, from where she received two pints of the best grade milk, free of any charge. Pimbo of course, delivered the milk, but she was not regarded as a cash customer on his round book. However, through a blunder by the office accounts, over a long period the cost of the milk had been transferred to Pimbo's round book, thus, the cost of Miss Rose's best grade was added to Pimbo's weekly takings, making, of course, a mounting weekly deficit. As Mr Hall's main job was to manage the dairy outdoor staff, he knew nothing about the accounts side, other than the figures given him by the accounts clerk.

"How did you find out about the mistake?" asked Jenny.

Albert smiled. "I accidently missed out her delivery, she 'phoned the dairy. Noticing the milk was not registered as cash in Pimbo's book, I tackled the accounts clerk. I had in mind, of course, the problem about your husband's short-ages. To my surprise, unwittingly, of course, the clerk had been placating the cost on to Pimbo's round book!"

By now, Pimbo had returned home to find an excited Jenny, almost in a celebration mood. On hearing the story, Pimbo could hardly thank Albert enough, the whole affair had almost made him leave the job, it seemed so ridiculous that the rift could have gone on for so long, without someone cottoning on, on the other hand maybe, he should have checked up on Miss Rose's free pints!

The milk round continued to be, at times, an exciting experience. A lady in the bottom end of Glisson Road who, though seemingly, had very few in her family, managed to have eight pints daily, was suddenly missing from her home. The Cambridge Evening News gave a good reason for the lady's sudden absence. The address turned out to be a house of ill-fame, the police had kept a close watch, then suddenly had swooped. Amazingly, most of the clients, to allay suspicion, never used the front entrance, but climbed a fence leading into the back entrance. Ironically, the lady was a lovely person, but being a widow, lack of money proved too much for her!

Then too, was the old lady in Tenison Avenue,

who, on pay day, appeared at the door with her
milk book. Although sporting a housekeeper, the
old dear was on only half-a-pint daily, which
amounted to 1/11d weekly. After Pimbo had
receipted the book, she would hold it close to her
eyes, for what seemed ages, in order to confirm
the signature as the old girl would examine the
penny, holding it up and testing it with her teeth!

On her sudden death, Pimbo found out from the
housekeeper, that candles consisted of her only
lighting; meals were extremely frugal. But, sadly,
although the little housekeeper had been with her
for thirty years, there had been no attempt to
arrange accommodation for the loyal servant. The
house was sold within a few months, and it was
only through the kindness of the local church that
the housekeeper was found a place in which to
live.

Fun of course crept into a milkman's lot.
Outside a house, again in Tenison Avenue, Pimbo
was called for emergency help. A lodger, living in
a small attic room at the top of a set of winding,
creaking stairs, had a fatal heart attack. He was a
very large man, of some sixteen stone or more.
The undertaker's staff of two men were having a
good deal of trouble in negotiating the stairs with
such a cumbersome burden.

To Pimbo's surprise, the pair had been unable,
because of the man's size, to place the lid on the
coffin-shell, it was a terrifying ordeal for the
young milkman, as he shouldered the massive
weight, turning the corners at times almost
tipped the body out of its container; in a reflex
action to avoid complete disaster, Pimbo found his

hands holding down the still warm body — only his war time experiences kept him going, and at the end of it all — a half-crown for his troubles!

Notes in milk bottles needed to be seen to be believed! 'No milk today, or tomorrow, and Thursday. Then, no more until further notice', 'On milk today' (the lady had an early morning hang-over for this gem). Another poor hapless housewife wrote 'From today, can I please have 'sterile' milk, as I now have a new mouth to feed!'

One morning, a lady living in Tenison Road came out. "I understand that you have a little girl, I'd like to get her an Easter egg, what's her name, then I can get it inscribed on the egg!"

On the Easter week, out came the lady with a gorgeous egg, handing it over to Pimbo, she almost floored him with — "That'll be 3/6 please!" Pimbo found out later that the woman kept a little sweet-shop somewhere in the Newnham area!

Tenison Road housed many wonderful characters, one such, a Mrs Harris, whose family later rose as fashion tycoons in several smart shops in the town centre. The dear old lady, despite her sons aptitude to change, still did her washing in the old fashioned way. A friend of Pimbo's, a Mr Kent, who was just starting up as a Hoover washing machine rep., tried very hard to supply Mrs Harris with a new way of washing — but, as far as Pimbo knew, the old lady still carried on with her old method of washing clothes. Pimbo found during school holidays, that his milk float acted as a kind of pied-piper. Children came out from all angles, following him until his round was finished.

Susan Kipping, daughter of Professor Kipping of Glisson Road, was one of Pimbo's ardent fans, so much so, that one afternoon, from his garden, he could see a school girl riding aimlessly around as though lost. To his surprise, it was Susan, "I just popped over, I heard that you lived somewhere around here!" she explained. But Pimbo made it clear that he wouldn't be expecting her around again.

Susan's family were great tennis enthusiasts, with a large tennis court in their grounds, Professor Kipping was a leading figure in Cambridge tennis tournaments.

Pimbo's old skeleton that of 'winning things' cropped up, one morning just as he was finishing his round, a large lorry, laden with milk churns, drew up. A rough-looking character thrust his head through his cabin window, "Could you use a churn, mate?"

Pimbo blinked. The driver explained. "I can get you one a week, full churn, there's a bomb in it — just say the word, no questions asked. The milk rationing's got the old gal's eating out of our hands — don't you want to be in it?"

Shaking his head, the young milkman moved away in disgust.

There was something about a milkman's job that few people realised. Each day, at the commencement of his round, Pimbo became an actor. The whole area, Tenison Road, Glisson Road, Lynewode Road, St Barnabas, was his stage, and his customers, the cast of a huge play, embracing love, laughter, tears, comedy, and life.

The little row of houses in Caius Terrace, at the

top end of Glisson Road, in the centre, lived a married couple, who were starting out as book-makers. Pimbo watched as furtive figures scurried in the little passageway, to put on their two-bobs and half-crowns, sometimes to win, at others, to bring a little more despair into their lives.

There was Mr Flesch, coming in after the war from the fate of a refugee to open up a little bed and breakfast place in Tenison Road.

Dear old Miss Hicks, Glisson Road, struggling against a diminishing income, which, once, was sufficient to bring her a little of life's comfort. Now, she would most politely inquire of Pimbo if he knew of anyone who might buy one of her hand-made stuffed animals, to offset rent rises, and a lower standard of living.

There was the little row of houses leading up into Station Road. Young mothers, with toddlers hanging on to their skirts, would appear on pay day, to tell Pimbo of their coming luck in getting a Council house. Every penny would be handed over with a slight reluctance, as they dreamt of the furniture they would require in their new house.

Then, too, of the young mother in Lynewode Road, whose husband had just a little time to spend with her at lunch time. To lengthen this precious time, she chose to feed the baby after he'd gone back from lunch — the only time she'd done this!

When she went to pick up the baby from her pram, the baby was dead — strangled by its own harness!

There were, of course, bad payers. One lady,

During school holidays, Pimbo's milk float acted as a kind of Pied Piper to the children.

after he'd called at the house several times to get his money, decided to pay a little at a time. This took a few weeks to clear up the debt. On the final payment, she confidently whispered into Pimbo's ear, "I'll bet you have a job to get your money off some of them?"

Then again, there were saucy occasions. One lady called out, "Come in" in answer to Pimbo's knock. On entry, he found the good lady in a state of undress, declaring calmly, "Sorry, I thought you were someone else!"

Many stories were bandied about milkmen and their so-called fancy pieces. But, Pimbo soon found out that unless the milkman actually aided and abetted a housewife's advances, nothing would come of it — it took two to make a bargain! A man's character was too much at stake, to allow such happenings to ruin it.

Pimbo watched youngsters grow up and bring credit to their parents. He saw old couples lose their spouses, and carry on until they, too, went to join their partner. He cut hedges for proud spinsters, who no longer could wield their shears. Yes, being a milkman helped one to become a philosopher, write books, or be better prepared for his own married life!

CHAPTER 8

Mother's Sunday

Christine was becoming a bonny child. Large brown eyes, dark hair and a sturdy little body. She made friends with most of the other tiny tots of the neighbourhood, and although the garden gate was usually tied up against her straying on to the road, she managed usually to get out into a neighbour's garden.

Pimbo was busily attending to his tomato plants, as Christine ambled up to him. "Richard is deaded!" she said in a flat voice. Jenny, from inside the kitchen, having heard the remark, came white-faced up to Pimbo, "What does she mean?"

During play sessions in the garden, when friends took turns in accommodating the children, Pimbo remembered that Christine had often played with a fair-haired little boy, whom he was sure was called Richard. They both stared unbelievingly at each other. Walking on to the pathway outside their home, they turned into Braybrooke Road, where Richard lived. A small knot of people were standing at the bus stop opposite Richard's home. A police car, ambulance, and a

worried-looking bus driver were in earnest conversation.

A friend, passing the scene, came up to Pimbo
and Jenny. "He was crossing the road, ran out
from behind the bus, you can guess the rest —
another tragedy we can do nothing about!"

Back in the garden, they looked at Christine.
Her introduction to death at such a young age,
was taken care of by her sheer innocence
Richard's deaded!" she said again, but somehow
her parents thanked God that the true implica-
tion had not entered deeply into her soul. They
thanked God, too, that it wasn't their child killed.

That week at the church on the corner of
Coldham's Lane, Mother's Day was being celebrated. Christine was all excitement as she was
getting ready for the special occasion. Pimbo, with
'tips' to augment his basic wage, was earning
about £6 to £7 weekly. Jenny had sacrificed
something from his wage to be able to purchase
from Eaden Lilley's a lovely little dress, making
Christine into a veritable little fairy. It was a
pretty sight, as the children, cordoned off into
their own kind, made their way into the church.
Tiny tots, clutching their little posies, wild and
multi-coloured flowers were abundant in splendid
array. Facing the church, the Church End part of
the estate could be seen glistening in the morning
sun, their prefabricated homes sprouting up like
mushrooms, as the field on which the prefabs
stood, once was a hunting ground for clandestine
mushroom gatherers.

Jenny, looking around at the sea of young
mothers, wondered had they been as she, waiting

for their lovers to come home from the war, fighting for a home, perhaps sitters-in for confused old people. Pimbo was looking resplendant in his demob suit, still as smart as ever, a nice grey stripe, as seen in the pre-war gangster films, she could almost hear Cagney's 'you dirty-rat' as soon as he put it on!

Cherryhinton was growing. Mr Ling had smartened up the front of his shop, with a nice glass panelled door, pity it was, that a careless customer, leaving it open on a windy day, caused the whole glass structure to be blown out.

Now, everyone was seated in the lovely old church. A nice children's hymn opened the service. Then there were prayers for little Richard, a prayer for the Co-op butchery manager, who had been stricken down with polio. A prayer for the community at large, that the new residents might live in harmony. The children were trooped out into another building, so they, too, might enjoy the service in keeping with their tiny minds.

The minister was gracious in his sermon. He hoped that the church might grow; that a terrible war had scarred the souls of many, that may well have attended church more regularly. But, this was a new beginning, old soldiers from two previous wars had hoped for 'an England fit for heroes to live in', God, in little Cherryhinton, was offering just that!

But it had to be reached out for, you had to take it with both hands! You had to offer it for your children, send them to Sunday school, they deserve to be taught that which kept their parents going through a long hard war!

After the service, Pimbo and Jenny, with Christine in her push-chair, walked around the village; Pimbo, who had played football against Cherryhinton in pre-war days, found so much had changed. The football pitch had gone under a deluge of bricks and mortar. Tiny thatched cottages that once graced the High Street, had disappeared. The railway cottage was still in existence, with the one-legged signalman still doing his exacting time-watching job of protecting the public from the on-coming trains.

On the way back to 180 Church End, the happy couple took in the pleasant scene, as they viewed other young couples, complete with their offspring walking around the estate. The lovely green lawns, resplendant with a blaze of colourful flowers, was of great contrast to the destruction of landscapes they had seen during the war years.

Penny Orders, their neighbour a few doors away, met them with a worried look. "Chas. has to go into hospital, I wonder if you could keep an eye on my little one, it's visiting day, Mum can't make it until tomorrow — it's his chest again!"

Rodney, Penny's little boy, dark haired (with ringlets) played well with Christine, so Jenny had few qualms about taking in the boy. Chas. Orders, whose health had been very up and down; at the time was a taxi-driver, earning a very precarious living. When hospitalised, Penny's entire family shared their sympathy, their time, and whatever they could 'chip in' with Penny. As Jenny confided with Pimbo, "I don't know what would happen should you be ill!" — But her young husband knew that the old war-time spirit still existed! —

and that Penny and Chas. would reciprocate all that had been done for them.

Twice a week, the little village would be inundated with the more relaxed patients from the nearby Fulbourn Hospital. They would, in escort with a couple of senior nurses, be taken into the village shop for their weekly ration of sweets or such-like goodies. Quite a few Fulbourn nurses lived in Cherryhinton, some on the new Council Estate, some sprinkled along the High Street.

Christine would stare in open-mouth style as the little band of patients, some holding hands, toured the village on their special outing day; she seemed a little jealous that they had such an easy passage to the sweet counter. One of the shop assistants was telling Jenny, "I've worked here for years, I know most of the faces, soon as one is missing, I say, where's old so-and-so, usually the nurse has a sad story to tell, they're like children really, wouldn't harm a soul!"

Pimbo came home that day with unexpected news. Stetchworth Dairies were selling out to a Strutt & Parker company. It meant the closing down of the dairy! Worse still, poor Mr Hall was found to be suffering from a terminable illness of the throat. Little Willy Carpenter, a well-loved roundsman had recently died, just a few years after retirement, and Pimbo had secured himself a new job with Betterwear, the brush people.

Well, I never!" replied Jenny with a smile. "It's like our old army days, just as we're settled, we get moved on — it's a good job we've been well trained.

Pimbo hesitated a little as his young wife

finished her short monologue. "One thing about the job, Jenny, I don't get a regular wage, I pay my own insurance — it's a commission-only job! Mr Webb, the local manager, is coming round to see us, I'm sure you'll like him, he's a real nice man!"

Mr Webb, a small, puckish faced individual, smiled at Jenny, as she bade him sit down, and then proffered the usual cup of tea.

"I can understand young wives being a little apprehensive!" he began, "But you must understand that although there is no basic wage neither is there any ceiling as to how much your husband could earn. The American firm, Fuller's, which is a counterpart of our firm Betterwear, control brush sales all over America, there's no reason why we can't do the same!"

Jenny frowned. "But no wage at all, suppose Pimbo is unable to achieve the sales, what about the rent, the food, we have a young child to support, a home to build, I feel that it's too much of a risk!"

Pimbo was in deep thought. Jenny was right! In true woman's logic, she had hit the nail on the head. But, on the other hand, the firm *was* new, at some time, even Fuller's had to strike out in a pioneering vein. Suppose he *could make good sales, suppose he could* build up a good living. It was the same as a franchise really; Betterwear supplied the goods that he sold; each week he paid them for their supplies, keeping back his own commission, which stood at one third of the rental price. There would be monthly bonuses, and a big bonus at the end of the year. One snag, as Mr Webb had pointed out, should a customer default on payment for the goods ordered, then Pimbo would have to make up the loss with his own cash, a large order from a customer might well turn out to be suspect, which could make a hole in his weekly wage!

Mr Webb sprang to his feet. "There's only one answer — try out the job with me in the morning, I'll fit you up with a full case of brushes, I'll introduce you to the customers, you'll do the actual selling, I'm sure by the end of the day, you will know whether or not you're a born salesman!"

Next morning, true to his word, the little manager arrived with Pimbo's working equipment. The case was similar to an ordinary suitcase, the difference being that the inside of the top half of the case housed such things as: toothbrushes, combs, pastry brushes, nail brushes, hair brushes and similar knick-knacks. The bottom half being fairly deep, held broom heads, hand brushes, mops, polishes, and cob-web or window brushes. The case was very heavy, but the advantage was that many items could be displayed with greater potential for sales.

The couple began at a little group of cottages on the right hand side of the road leading into Fulbourn village.

It soon became apparent to Pimbo that Mr Webb had visited the area a few times before, and that his cheerful, casual approach fitted admirably into door-to-door selling.

"It's the new man, Mr Unwin. He'll be taking over from me, you'll find him a good lad, so look after him, won't you?" said the manager, kindly.

"Looking after him" usually resulted in the sale

of a tin of polish or a small brush the average sale working out at about three-shillings per head, meaning that Pimbo had earned a shilling at each sale.

"Not bad" pointed out the little manager, "that's ten-bob you've earned in a short time, should you keep this up for the rest of the day — well, you work it out?"

Pimbo smiled back. "But these sales could be just sympathy sales, you know, with your presence influencing the customer — I'll tell you what, leave me on my own, let me see what I can do without your help, then come and see me in the morning, I'll tell you then whether or not I'll take the job!"

Pimbo enjoyed the next phase of the day's selling. It seemed that Mr Webb had built up a good honest relationship with his customers. The brushes were hard-wearing, and replaced at any dissatisfaction from the customer. The sales Pimbo made, although not too high in price, never-the-less were substantial, as Mr Webb pointed out, "Polishes are your bread and butter lines — they are not likely to be refuted on pay day, anything else, treat as a bonus, that way, the customers will appreciate low pressure selling as opposed to the foot-in-the-door tactics of the high pressure sharks!"

At the end of the day, Pimbo had sold enough to earn himself four pounds; a six day week would bring in a wage of £24 — then, realising that one day would have to be allocated for delivery, thus bringing it down to £20, he also had to allow for bad weather, but even allowing for such obstacles,

Pimbo felt that the job potential was good, by working hard, with bonuses included, he could give Jenny the things she needed bo build up the home, then, too, wasn't it a chance for Pimbo to make something of himself, something extra for Christine — one day he might be able to start upon his own!

That evening, to avoid waiting in for Mr Webb, Pimbo bussed up to the manager's home at the top of Castle Street. Mrs Webb, a matronly type woman, let him into a small room in the centre of a dimly lit passageway. Mont'Ely's little barber's shop was just a few doors away from the Webb's home.

The Betterwear manager showed little surprise at Pimbo's acceptance of the job. "I knew you were the right lad for the job." Producing from a small cupboard a large carton, he pulled out handfuls of small items: Minature tins of polish, which were suitable for polishing doll's house furniture, bottle openers, small tubes which, pressed into the side of a soap-powder carton, would act as perfect pourers, plastic spoons, knitting measures, and various kinck-knacks for domestic use, Mr Webb handed over to his new salesman.

"Free gifts!" beamed the little man. "Usually you buy them as you order your goods — but, I'll give you a kick off with a few — they make good sales gimmicks, we reckon that a good successful salesman over the years, is also a good purchaser of free gifts! Allowing you to work out your notice at the milk round, I'll expect you here to collect your case in a week's time!"

Jenny took Pimbo's decision philosophically.

"You can but try, should it fail, you can always try for another job — we can do with extra cash — and another thing — !" she finished with a cheeky grin, "I think there's another mouth to feed on the way!"

Pimbo's last week at the dairy was a sad departure. Little gifts were left at the door beside the empty milk bottles. He would miss the customers, the friendly chats, the cups of tea. Then, too, the dairy staff felt it badly, some had been at the dairy for many years.

Poor Mr Hall died that very week, as though he, too, had filled out his final notice!

Mr Tupling was going into hospital for an operation. Pimbo felt that the old boy was more than due for a complete rest. It meant, too, that Mrs Hall would be going back to her grass-roots, to a London which, no doubt, she would find difficult to recognise, but would be back into the watchful fold of her grandchildren, now grown up, but with families of their own.

For Pimbo and Jenny it was another new start. Just like their war days, move, settle, move, settle, new faces, sad departures. He smiled as he thought of Christine. For her it would mean very little, thank goodness, she was too young to worry about such things.

He wondered how poor old Noah was getting on, then, Molly Bishop came to mind. If he could earn enough in a few years, he might be able to buy a small car, he could visit all his old friends. Mr Webb had a nice car, bought from his early earnings as both rep. and manager.

Jenny liked the idea. As soon as Christine

"It's the new man, Mr Unwin. He'll be taking over from me!" said Mr Webb.

started school proper, she could help Pimbo with his deliveries, cycling on an old trade's bike, would be hard work on delivery day, but a nice little car would make it so much easier!

But, as Pimbo pointed out, should there be another one 'on the way' well then, the partnership of Pimbo and Jenny would have to be delayed a while longer!

"STAFFORDSHIRE STREET IN THE TWENTIES!"

From Mahoney's you buy bloater paste,
Broken biscuits at the Co-op way down.
For bread, to procure a wholesome taste,
It's Taylor's, for yesterday's brown,
St Matthew's, Church tower, booms out "Five",
Of the clock, you'll be thinking of teas,
Bowie O'dell's, calls, keep the street alive,
As Bill Haines, from his home, sells "Hot Peas",
Top of the street, stands a Dicken's-type Inn,
"George the Fourth," your memory to jog;
Boarding, Irish navvies, and guzzlers of gin,
Its landlady, tough Molly Hogg,
The White heads, Canham's, Page's, and Brading,
Anderson's, Nunn's, Kelly's and Deard's,
Paint a live picture, alas, gradually fading,
Into fond memories of yesteryears!

Fred Unwin

CHAPTER 9

The Coronation

With Pimbo's extra money coming in from his normal pay and bonuses with the Betterwear firm, Jenny was able to procure some furniture and carpetry in order to comply with her long yearned-for wish 'for a nice home of her own'.

Dupont's and Blundell's were retail firms cashing in on the new demand for 'something different', which young housewives could have on 'tick', paying a little each week, and thus, slowly building up their homes.

Also, young men, home from the wars, without the benefit of pre-training apprenticeships, were able to put on a smart suit, somehow procure an old banger, and thus set out on a means of gaining a livelihood. It was long hours, tedious book-work, with an ex-sergeant major as boss to gee them up for new orders. A familiar sight, on a working-class estate, would be a solitary car laden with polythene wrapped goodies, standing outside a group of houses, with a young man perpetually running in and out with his polythene parcels, sometimes up until 10 p.m.

Jenny found that at times, the salesmen could

be a little too persuasive. Having answered the
door to a couple of canvassers from one of the
retail door-to-door firms, she casually inquired
the price of several commodities. Without actually
giving an order, Jenny saw the men leave the
house.

Two evenings later, with Pimbo home, and
watching the television, Jenny thought she'd
heard a noise coming from the kitchen.

"It's next-doors kids, getting their ball from the
back — don't bother!" Pimbo, rather lazily, dis-
missed his young wife's forebodings.

However, later, on entering the kitchen to prepare an evening drink, Pimbo found a large parcel
on the kitchen table, which contained the items
that Jenny had queried the price of. "It's sharp
practice!" said a rather cross Jenny. I'll leave
them just as they are, we'll see what the outcome
is; without knocking the door, they had dumped
the stuff on to the table, hoping they could get
away with it!"

True to form, on Monday morning, the regular
tally-man for Jenny's area turned up. "I've
brought your payment card!" he said briskly. "I've
entered in the goods you ordered. I hope you found
everything in apple-pie order, should you require
more vouchers, don't be afraid to ask!"

Jenny placed the large brown paper parcel into
a very surprised salesman's arms. "I didn't order
these items. Your canvassers tried dumping them
on me — so I'm dumping them back from whence
they came — good-day to you!"

Another trick going the rounds was that of
photography! A smart pair of slicksters would

approach the unwary young mother with the seductive tale of a competition for childrens' photographs. It was a 'free entry' and the winners would receive a special prize. Within a week or so, they would return with beautifully framed pictures, pictures that a young mother could hardly refuse, coloured plates of their youngsters; putting into the background a long war, rationing and the struggle to survive; the pictures depicted a rise above all this, and a pioneering peep into the families future. The framed portraits were pricey, the contract for weekly payments was handed over to the likes of the door-to-door retail firms. But, a peep into the sitting-rooms of the majority of homes on the vast new estates, would find a framed coloured portrait of the family offspring, proudly cocking a snoop at the poor in spirit!

It was their very own little bit of heaven!

So, in fairness to the Blundell's and Dupont's, they were bringing into the reach of poor families, things which they otherwise would be unable to procure. Providing they kept their budget in line with income and expenditure, they could furnish their homes in a way which their parents and grandparents could never achieve.

One night, Jenny happily informed Pimbo of her expected pregnancy. It meant another move; as the prefab boasted only two bedrooms, also, in view of the current demob categories, two bedroom accommodation was the greater in demand, thus leaving a move into a three-bedroom house much easier for a harassed Housing Officer to arrange. After a few visits to the Guildhall Hous-

ing Department, the Unwins', one happy morning, recieved the key to No. 15, Keynes Road,
Cambridge.

It was a large estate, tucked away behind the
Pye Telecommunications factory. Sprawling and
bedraggled, with the debris from finished homes,
vying with the masses of material standing ready
for the newly started houses. Keen young husbands, with the 'winning ways' of the Army still in
the blood, made full use at week-ends of the left
over building materials. Garden paths sprung up
like mushrooms overnight. Clothes line posts
were cemented in from the conveniently lying
sacks of 'Portlands special'. Some even attempted
shed erection from the masses of wood partitions,
which graced the outside of half erected Council
homes.

All this, however, came to an aburpt halt!

An over-ambitious Council tenant, legitimately
borowed a brand new wheelbarrow from a soft-
hearted foreman, promising it would be returned
on the ensuing Monday. Finishing his special job,
the intial borrower lent out the barrow to his
neighbour, who, alas, loaned out the barrow to
someone not in the near vicinity. A frustrated and
irate foreman could be seen visiting every home in
Keynes Road searching for the missing barrow.
Consequently, the 'winning' borrowing, or even
stealing was clamped down on.

Many had to pull up their paths, tug out their
clothes line posts, and give up tools or miscel-
laneous items mis-appropriated from the various
building sites.

In the meantime, Jenny's pregnancy had

reached an advanced stage, so much so, that on ringing up the Maternity Ward at Mill Road, Pimbo was told that he had become the father of a bonny bouncing boy of some eight pounds, and that he could visit his wife during ordinary visiting times.

The next hour was spent by an excited Pimbo in ringing up relatives and close friends, telling them of the happy event.

The bus seemed as though it would never come, but, at last the dutiful young husband found himself at the Porter's Lodge, inquiring the name of the ward in which Jenny awaited him. "Ward Six, Bed 23!" rapped out a cheerful porter, "and the best of British luck!"

At the entrance to the ward, a slight delay seemed apparent, as visitors were held back, until a pretty young nurse informed Pimbo, "Your wife has just finished feeding the baby — you may go in !"

With searching eyes, Pimbo scanned the ward of frilly-clad mothers, but somehow couldn't spot Jenny. Walking to the end of the double row of beds, he turned to the nurse. "But I can't see my wife, this is Ward 6 isn't it?"

Laughing kindly at his exasperated look, the nurse strolled across to a nearby bed. "There you are, Mrs Jenny Unwin, Bed 23, and you do live in Histon, do you not?" Pimbo just couldn't believe his eyes, Jenny Unwin of Histon, tried to keep a straight face. "I'm sorry!" she blushed. "Your wife must be in another ward, I remember her at pre-natal clinics, we laughed at the similarity of our names!"

Pimbo was fearing the worst, after having 'phoned up half of Cambridge, it was quite on the cards that Jenny hadn't even given birth —

A kindly matron confirmed the truth. "Mrs Jenny Unwin, 15 Keynes Road, is in Ward Seven, Bed Seven. At the moment she is in labour, I suggest you come back this evening. "I'm so sorry about the muddle, I hope it turns out to be a boy – it will save your re-phoning!"

The evening turned out to be one of joy. Keith Thomas Unwin added his name to the list of registered babies — and, as many people pointed out, 'they had managed the coveted pigeon-pair'!

Life went on rosily. The children around the small crescent grew up with each other. Ian and Wendy Ainsworth, Robin and Sheila White, the Arliss family with their three boys, Pip Smith, Tony and David White. Next door to Jenny lived the Rolls family, a kindly set of parents were Arthur and Millie, with Sidney and Ruth as their offspring.

Pimbo was working hard at Betterwear's. His bonuses helped cover any little treat they might desire — one such being a car!

"Yes, I'd like a car!" said Jenny. "I never thought I'd ever be in a position to get one. God's been good to us, with two youngsters to cart around, it would save bus fares!"

Pimbo answered the advertisement in the local paper. "Small car, Ruby Austin for sale. Must go to a person who would maintain it as thoroughly as present owner has done, over ten delightful years of ownership. Fully taxed for year. Bargain at £75 — owner must get a larger car — only reason for sale!"

The address in Hills Avenue, found Pimbo at the door of the car's owner. It was a little beauty, VE6660, and its bodywork was as shiny as a shilling on a sweep's face. The upholstery, maroon (Jenny's favourite colour) was in magnificient condition. It was coach built, the only distinct feature which might put off a prospective buyer, was its large wheels in lieu of the usual small, almost toylike ones of the Baby Austin.

"Only three of its kind were over built!" put in the owner, a kindly looking young man, whose main use of the car was to see that his aged mother got about! "They had a special demonstration on New Square — then came the war, and no more were put on the assembly line — it breaks my heart to sell it!"

Pimbo snapped it up for three reasons. It was in perfect nick. The engine was simple in design. A small car was more suitable for a rather rusty driver like himself!

"One thing!" said the past owner as the notes were counted out in his hands. "I want you to promise to bring the car back here after six months. I want to know that it's being looked after!"

As he looked back for a moment before driving away, Pimbo was certain that the fellow was actually crying — a real 'Baby' Austin, thought its new owner.

Jenny was delighted at the appearance of their new car. She fondled the shiny bonnet and kept flicking on the indicator arm which pushed out from the side of the door's framework. Sitting in

the passenger seat, she looked up at Pimbo, who,
sitting well back in the driver's seat, was pretend-
ing to be a man of wealth by tapping an imaginary
cigar's ash into the portable ash-tray on the dash-
board.

They both looked around the little crescent near
their home. The houses of the local postman, the
Dewhurst butcher, the bus driver, the insurance
man; Jim Stewart, White, Smith and Ainsworth
in respective order, with nice tidy gardens. The
postman often fought verbal duals with the
youngsters, whose footballs strayed into his prize
crop of dahlias.

Of those mentioned, only Tom Ainsworth owned
a car.

"Do you think the neighbours will feel that
we're trying to be too hoity-toity?" asked Jenny. "I
mean, with our new telly, now a car, it makes me
feel guilty!"

Putting his arm around Jenny's shoulder, Pimbo smiled back. "We've got what we've earned. I
took a chance on a no basic wage job. Many men
would fight shy of such a job. No, Jenny, years
ago, I never dreamt that one day we would own
our own car, now we can take the kids out, even go
to the seaside on a Sunday, instead of relying on
the excursions!"

Jenny had small tears welling into her eyes. "I'll
tell you what! Next week is the Coronation, it's
going to be shown on telly. The whole street will
be on holiday — what say we invite the neighbours in, it'll be our way of showing them that
we're still with our feet on the ground!"

Pimbo gave her a quick kiss. "You're right!

Our's is the only telly in the street. I'll make out little invitation notes, we'll open up the sliding door, we can have tea and biscuits during the interval, it'll be the old Kinema all over again.

Coronation Day was wet and miserable. With everything spick and span, Jenny waited at the side of the window, hoping their invitations would not fall on stony grond.

At first it was an influx of only youngsters; Jenny began to despair. Then first one parent, and another, came to 'see' if their offsprings were behaving 'proper and correct like'. Soon, practically every parent from Keynes Road (Pimbo's half) were crowded into the sitting room; with the dining room acting as an annexe, Pimbo sacrificially promised to be tea-maker!

He counted the heads — sixty in all, not including the youngsters. Looking around the room, he suddenly realised how nice it was that the spirit shown during the war years, had now loomed to the surface. The military splendour moving across the tiny screen, the colourful gaiety of the occasion, the wrapt earnest faces with rent arrears, domestic problems pushed under the carpet; as the wonderful pageantry of marching columns swept along.

"Two spoons or one?" "No milk, please, in my coffee!" "Just one biscuit, I'm on a diet, you know." Suchlike pleasantries flashed across the room as Pimbo, with one eye on the screen, handed out the many cups of tea. Then, too, he saw a little cluster of wrapped presents, brought in by several parents, as a 'little something for having us in'!

The 1953 Coronation Year had lifted a load

1953, Coronation Year, had lifted a load from many an aching heart!

from many an aching heart. Somehow, from the sea of faces staring at the screen, the past war had been pushed back into its perspective. England was strong again, although the falling rain had done its best to dampen spirits, the colourful pageantry, as a rainbow, had nullified a wet afternoon into a glorious occasion.

Catching Pimbo's eye, Jenny moved into the kitchen. Alone, the young couple stared at each other. "It wasn't like that at all, was it, Pimbo?" They gave me lovely little presents, there was no thought of malice, about our having the first telly in the street — do you know, we've got to stop being narrow minded!"

Pimbo laughed. "It's our background, you see, we've been so used to having nothing, that we feel guilty having something. One thing, though, I would trade it all in for our two kids, they come first!"

"Your Keith's fighting!" came a voice from the lounge. Jenny laughed as she scampered through to prevent another 'war'!

CAMBRIDGE FAIR

We hasten our steps, as the music
Wafts through the darkened night.
Joyful cries from the youngsters,
Push worries, and care, to flight!

Tis, Cambridge Fair, that beckons,
Flashing neons, break through the mist.
Feelings of joy, come over me,
It's something I cannot resist!

From Fair Street, to the Common,
The happy throngs, still come.
The childrens' pockets jingle,
With pennies saved by Mum!

We cast off bleak old Winter,
Shrug away, cough, and wheeze,
To soothe our ails with music,
From the Fairground melodies!

Carousels, have power to quiet,
Our restless pulse of care.
Candy-floss, and side-show treats,
Are joys, beyond compare!

Fair-nights are filled with laughter,
As bump-cars swerve their way,
Then, laden with rock and nougat,
We happily steal away!

Fred Unwin

CHAPTER 10

Life Goes On

Betterwear, ever on the look-out for sales gimmicks, chose what Pimbo thought to be — a 'grand winner' — a symbol of the Coronation year, complete with the Royal insignia on the back of a new type clothes brush at 9/7d — it appeared to be a real humdinger! And so it was — until Pimbo made his way into Devonshire Road!

Devonshire Road, a long narrow street of houses on one side, and the clatter and hiss of rolling stock on the other — a true railwayman's territory. But over the years, the houses changed hands, the older residents died, and the majority of houses took on sub-letting, bed-sitters; and, on that particular day of Pimbo's visit, every other house seemed to be putting up airmen from the American services.

Many of them were due for home leave, some for complete demob — they fell hook-line-and-sinker for the clothes brush, which would tell their families that they, the airmen, had been in England on such a truly historic occasion; the Piltsdown Man hoax, which shocked the world that same year, had nothing on the shock that Pimbo was in store for!

"Sure buddy, I'll have six!" "Order me a dozen, pal, my family back home will think it a wow!" "You English , you know your history — I'll get me half-a-dozen!" "Why, back in the States, these will sell like hot cookies, can you get me a box of fifty?" — And so it went on!

So, on that particular morning, Pimbo took orders for dozens of the new selling line. Betterwear had a system whereby the salesman sent in his order a week in advance. The goods arrived by rail, and then by B.R. Goods van, in time for the week-end delivery. Every item ordered by the salesman would have to be paid for, the remainder of the money collected, one third, would be his.

A big snag was that should there be any default of payment, the salesman would bear the loss!

Pimbo began his delivery of the new clothes brush at around four o'clock on a Thursday evening, prior to the next day being Good Friday! Shock after shock was to follow!

"Sorry, haven't been paid yet, we get paid monthly, that was last week; so you've got a long wait, buddy!"

"Leave the brush, come back in three weeks, Uncle Sam won't let you down!" And so it went on. It gradually dawned on Pimbo that a Yankee would pay on the nail, provided that you were standing over him on pay day! First come, first served, to the devil the hindmost!

A sad Pimbo ruminated over the boxes of Coronation 1953 clothes brushes. Of the vast order, only three had been successfully placated, his wage for the week's work was nil — he was many pounds out, which would have to be made good — as Jenny laconically pointed out, "My dear, you've been given the *brush* !"

Worse still, as a kindly neighbour put to the young salesman, "You won't see many of these on next pay day, there's a very strong rumour that the boys are moving to Lakenheath!"

Despite this set-back, Pimbo found himself leading salesman for the district, and in due course received a silver cup in recognition of his achievement; a proud Mr Les Pulfer, the Cambridge Manager, presented it at the Area meeting.

Pimbo found much to amuse him whilst on his brush round. One lady, crippled with arthritis, would bid him, in a loud voice, to enter her small Council house. The lady, apparently, used but one room in the house, in which she slept, cooked and watched a small twelve-inch telly. On his way through to her, Pimbo noticed the derelict appearance of the hall, stairway and kitchen. Dust, cobwebs and newspapers, yellow with age, might well have been used for prop's in a Hitchcock thriller. The young salesman put it all down to the poor lady's crippling disease.

The room in which she lived was on a par with the rest of the house, the customer eyed Pimbo curiously. "I've dealt with your firm for many years, I've just moved in from Romford, so I'll expect you to keep up my polish order — one large tin, every month, can you do that, my man?"

Pimbo blinked. "Well of course, madam. I'll start you off today, then you'll be on my monthly roster. I take it you have the ordinary white wax?"

The lady nodded. Glancing around the room, the salesman took in the complete lack of furniture showing a semblance of polish. There was no lino gracing the floor, mostly reddicut half-finished rug monstrosities. Then, too, the hall, stairway was just as bereft of any signs of having received a welcome polish. Pimbo had to say it!

"Oh, by the way, madam, what do you find our polish most beneficial for?"

"It's my feet. I rub it well in, all round my ankles, I swear by it, I do. My old mum, put me up to it, used for years, she did. I suppose it's the linseed and paraffin what does it!"

Polish, of course, was what brush salesman called their 'bread and butter line'. Pimbo was very thankful for his loyal polish customers: Dr Corston of Newmarket Road could be relied upon for a king-size tin every month, as did the New Square dentist, and Galloway & Porters; most of the pubs along Newmarket Road darkened their bar counters with either the lovely dark cream or the usual brown polish.

Many, many, households, took for granted their supply of furniture shiners, in the shape of duster, polish or cream. Of course there was laughter along the way!

The bad payer, who seemed really annoyed as Pimbo arrived on her doorstep at 7 a.m., just as she was leaving for her bedmaker's job. Despite calling at reasonable hours, often hearing voices from within, this lady failed to open her door at Pimbo's knock — so it had to be desperate situations, requiring desperate remedies — she paid!

Then there was the legitimate customer who was *never* in. After calling at least eight times without response, on the final call, the lady was just closing her front door, about to go shopping. "Oh, you're lucky to catch me!" she said blithely, "I was just going out!"

Again, was the delightful customer who, having run out into the street in order to catch Pimbo to order a 1/9d flue brush, was at home a fortnight later as the salesman delivered the brush.

Sitting at her kitchen table, with a bottle of stout nearby, and a newly opened packet of Players Twenty, she calmly announced, "Oh, I can't pay for it this week, you'll have to bring it back next Saturday!"

Pimbo blinked, thinking of a sixteen mile journey (there and back), on his trade cycle, which he used for delivery, he tried to make her see what she was letting him in for. But she remained adamant!

Thinking quickly, Pimbo took the brush round to the next door neighbour to whom he'd already delivered polish, and explained the situation.

Taking the brush, she paid over the 1/9d. "Why, the old skin-flint, I'll make her sit up, getting you to come all this way again — only last week she won £100 on the football pools!"

Pimbo made a hasty retreat as the furious lady neighbour sped round with brush in hand to the defaulting customer. He vowed then and there never to call on *that* woman again!

Bad payers, were, luckily, few and far between. Pimbo devised a certain plan in order to combat this weekly salary reducing nuisance. Should the order be anything up to £3, the goods, instead of being ordered, would be taken from his demonstration case, then, were the customer to default,

Pimbo would not have to pay from his weekly income.

One customer proved an exception to the rule! The house was dingy looking, dozens of dirty milk bottles outside the door; had the customer not beckoned him to her door, Pimbo would not have called on her. As she placed her order, a substantial one, of seven pounds; including a new bristle broom, and furniture mop, several untidy children appeared at the door. Pimbo had already made up his mind that this was going to be a 'case order'.

On the day of delivery, Pimbo approached the house with some misgiving.

The woman appeared at the door looking quite pleased at the sight of her new cleaning equipment, Pimbo busily arrayed the goods at her side.

"What's the damage?" she asked, firmly.

"Seven pounds, in all, madam!" replied the salesman, with tongue in cheek. To his surprise, the customer, pulling out a wad of notes, peeled off the required amount. "There you are, my man, and give me a call next time. I'll probably be needing a few more things!"

The only thing wrong with the set-up was that Pimbo had to go round minus a bristle broom and furniture mop until his replacement order came in!

Pimbo continued steadily on, winning cups and prizes for being leading district salesman; until, one day, at a monthly meeting of rep's, a new name headed the list, and what's more, the winning rep. turned out to be a lady!

Her sales were astronomical, far and away, volume-wise, to anything that Pimbo had ever

accomplished. Les Pulfer sat facing Pimbo. "But
how does she get her delivery in, she must have
help from the other rep's, no-one could deliver
such an amount?"

Pimbo nodded. "Well, we'll see what happens at
next month's meeting; if she's still going strong,
I'll take off my hat to her!"

The next month was full of surprises, not only
was the lady's name not on the prize list, but it
was not even on the list of sales-staff! To a
surprised meeting, the woman's manager explained. The lady worked in the Hackney Marshes
area during her phenomonal sales. A heavy flood-
ing of the marshes infiltrated into the homes of
hundreds of pre-fabs, destroying furniture and
domestic accessories, including brooms, brushes
and other household items — this made the
national newspapers.

An Insurance firm, perhaps to gain publicity,
announced that it would make good to the house-
holder most of the items which had been ruined
through the flood. Many women used this as an
opportunity to requip their homes with brand new
cleaning brushes and mops, from which the prize
winning saleslady picked up vast orders.

However, when the Insurance man came to
confirm payment for such, many were unable to
produce the ruined article — thus, receiving no
money with which to pay the brush-saleslady.
This was almost a replica of Pimbo's Coronation
clothes brush fiasco. Consequently, the poor saleslady couldn't get her orders out, and promptly
resigned!

Pimbo's clientele grew steadily. Most customers

were most appreciative at their suppliers little method of giving discount on large orders.

Betterwear brought out a new window cleaning brush, which entailed several small accessories. Connecting joints for the long pole to give it stability, a rubber sleeve to prevent water running down the users' arms, and such-like. The complete job ran out at almost £2, of this amount, 2/6d for the pole connection was thrown in by Pimbo as free.

The husband of one customer, however, accused Pimbo of overcharging. "Taking advantage of my wife!" he ranted, on Pimbo's appearance at the door on delivery day. "Now then, let me see your price list, and a copy of the invoice you gave my wife!"

A very red-faced husband, hardly able to stand still as the salesman went over each item, stared up at Pimbo, as, funnily enough, although no charge had been made for the connecting rod, Pimbo had actually *undercharged* for the whole unit!

"I don't want charity!" the man stormed. "Here, take the full amount, and don't call at my door again!" On which the customer paid over five shillings more than he'd bargained for!

A crafty wink from the wife, told Pimbo that she bore no malice, from then on she placed her orders with the next-door neighbour.

A very good rapport was built up, on the policy of the company's replacement of any undue bad wear of their product. However, even so, one very irate lady gave Pimbo cause for mirth.

During the first month of his employment, the

"It's my feet. I rub it well in, I swear by your polish!"
said the old lady.

firm withdrew a round tin of window polish, for
that of a smart square tin, which sold at 1/11d.
Several years passed by, until one morning, the
customer complained of poor service. "Fetch it to
me!" said Pimbo brightly, and after waiting at
least ten minutes, the lady appeared from the
bottom of her garden shed, holding up a round tin
of window polish, which of course was now a
defunct line. The tin had rusted over the years,

and a white paste had formed around the cracked seams of the aged tin.

"I want a replacement!" she said firmly.

With the window-brush husband still fresh in his mind, Pimbo wasn't having any!

"My dear lady, this tin is at least five years old. It originally cost 1/9d. and is no longer one of our lines — I suggest you purchase a new tin at 1/11d., I'm afraid a replacement is out of the question!"

The lady slammed the door shut.

Pimbo smiled as he made his way home. How lucky he was that nincty nine percent of his customers were grand folk, salt-of-the-earth, you might say!

THE PRIORY SCHOOL
(RAWLYN ROAD PRIMARY)

(Christine and Keith's first school)

From the Howard Estate they walk,
Across Newmarket Road — so wide,
Past Proctors' stores, in friendly talk;
With new satchels by their side.

To the Priory School they come,
With more than a little noise.
Nervous child, with anxious Mum;
First day, girls and boys!

Miss Gray, Head Ma'am, with kindly grace,
Receives them in her fold.
"I'm sure your child will stand the pace,
Reach heights, so far untold!"

It'll be stars, and ticks, maybe a cross,
And 'Miss said, this and that'.
Poor Mum, will soon bemoan the loss,
Of missing gloves, and hat!

With fund appeals, trips abroad,
Speech days, and special slippers.
Things, that Mum can ill afford;
Twas cheaper, when they were nippers

Fred Unwin

CHAPTER 11

The Shrubbery School

With the kids in bed, a roaring fire, and the tranquility of a peaceful evening, Pimbo and Jenny were in a reflective mood "You're earning good money!" Jenny was saying. "I think it time that we got to thinking about Christine's school life, she's not too happy at the Priory, it's a good little school, but Chris tells me that she can't hit if off with the teachers — I sometimes think that her headaches have something to do with her worry about going to school!"

Pimbo nodded. He often thought about his own schooldays. Although happy, his reading matter embraced many of the public school stories of the day. Harry Wharton of Greyfriars, Billy Bunter the Owl of the Remove, Bob Cherry, Mr Prout, Mr Quelch as junior masters and the stalwart Dr Locke as Head. He remembered a poem:

> The Head is worthy Dr Locke
> A man of endless learning,
> Who seeks to rule the famous school
> With wisdom that's discerning.

With Prout and Quelch to back him up,
He makes his pupils put in
The fundamental parts of Greek
And much-detested Latin.

Somehow, studies of their own, to Pimbo, was a dream that would never come true. Postal orders, whether pinched by Billy Bunter or not, to Pimbo meant wealth in abundance. The whole school set-up, with its flowing sports fields, marquees on Speech Day, house matches, was a seventh heaven to a boy from St Georges, East Road.

"Well!" said Jenny, laughing at her husband's trance-like appearance. "I never had much of a chance myself. I'd like to give Christine an opportunity to make something of herself — but what can we do — ?"

"We'll settle for the best within our purse range. The Shrubbery School is holding an entrance examination for junior. The school is fairly close-by, on Hills Road, opposite the Catholic Church. We'll go along, have a chat with the Head, Mrs Living-Taylor, find out the fees, and see what goes on from there!"

Spotting a line of classy limousines outside the little building of the Shrubbery, at first Pimbo and Jenny were reluctant to enter. Then, thinking once more that his wildest dreams might come true through his little daughter; Pimbo made a positive step into the Head's study.

Mrs Living-Taylor was a fine looking woman, with a habit of lifting one shoulder slightly above the other. Her husband, a dignified gentlemen, sat beside her, as she greeted the young couple.

Pimbo, whilst waiting to enter, had noticed a book of poems entitled 'Buttercups and Daisies' lying on a table strewn with Shrubbery School literature for parents.

"I see that you write poetry!" slipped in Pimbo, as a means of introduction, also noticing that the Master's wife had collared Jenny for her own.

Sitting down beside Mr Living-Taylor, Pimbo told of his aspirations as a boy to attend a private school, to savour that which had escaped him, his longing to be better educated — now, perhaps, the chance had befallen his daughter!

"My school is not one of class-distinction. Our sole aim is to prepare a child for life outside the school. We have a Christian basis for our curriculum, maths, science, English literature, may well be fundamental issues; but the thin red line running through all our activities, is the backbone for our boys and girls to tackle life's complexities — Oh, by the way, what is your business?"

Pimbo looked across to Jenny, who was in deep conversation with the Head. So this was the pay-off, he thought! He remembered the application form for another school he once had toyed with — at the bottom were the words: 'Please state your telephone number, in case your child is connected with any emergency.'

What could he say? Door-to-door salesman? Brush salesman, or Betterwear Representative? He had no telephone, although a close neighbour, Mrs Rumbelow, would always take calls!

"I'm waiting!" said the Master, kindly.

"I'm a door-to-door brush salesman!" blurted out Pimbo. "But I'm head salesman, I get good bonuses, I want my child to receive as good an education as possible — I, er — !"

"You needn't apologise, my man!" interposed the Master, kindly. "It's good to see young men thinking in such manner. You served your Country, I presume, then you deserve the best for your children; in the trenches there was no monopoly on telephones, status, or anything else. Should your child pass the entrance exam, well then, she can become a pupil at the Shrubbery school. What's more, we have a special fee for the parents with more than one child at the school — so you see, we do what we can for all and sundry!"

On the way home, Jenny told Pimbo of a similar kindness to that of the Headmaster. Mrs Living-Taylor had made her feel thoroughly at ease. Jenny was thinking of the words of a current song:

> 'When I was just a little girl
> I asked my mother what would I be?
> Will I be pretty, will I be rich?
> What will become of me?"

And the answer was:

> 'My dear, my dear, whatever will be *will* be
> The future's not mine to see,
> So my dear, my dear — !'

Jenny laughed at her thoughts; maybe, getting her daughter into the Shrubbery might help Christine on the way to something better; at least it wouldn't be for the lack of parental effort!

To her parents immense pleasure, Christine passed the Entrance Examination with flying colours, thus, she was due to begin at the Shrubbery at the commencement of a new term. The fees had been whittled down to the fact that Pimbo would have to work very hard, maintain his bonuses, and maybe as soon as Keith was old enough, he, too, could join his sister!

Mrs Naylor, Christine's teacher at her new school, was a popular member of the teaching staff. Firm and fair, she gave a very impressive report on Christine's progress. "We must try and get Keith in as well!" Jenny was saying. "Christine's smart uniform has made her brother a little jealous — I could take a job you know!"

Pimbo nodded in assent. "I didn't want you to work if possible, but it's for the sake of the kids. Pye's, at the top of the road, are taking on women, just part-time, eh, see how it goes?"

So it was; that Christine and Keith, clad in their smart red and grey uniforms, each morning boarded the bus which would drop them almost outside their school building — but disaster struck!

Mrs White, Jenny's next door neighbour, also went on the same bus; as she was putting to Jenny one afternoon, "I had to wake your Keith up this morning, fast asleep he was. Marvellous little chap though, bright as a button usually, chats away on the bus, I suppose he must have got a little over-tired!"

Over the tea table, after Jenny had told him about the incident, Pimbo decided that he would take the children to school himself. It would knock half-an-hour off their getting up time, save bus fares, and would leave only the return from school

as a bus journey. He smiled as he thought of the
first morning he took his son down to the bus-stop,
Christine was off school with an infected ear. As
the bus approached, Keith began to cry. "I haven't
done my dodgem's!" he replied on his dad's query.
"Mrs Naylor told me it was exam's today!"

Apparently, dodgem's was a method which the
Shrubbery taught on learning tables other than
parrot-like recitations. 'seven-sevens', 'nine-
sevens' and such like was a method of making
sure that the pupils *really* knew their tables. With
a kiss and reassurance that Mrs Naylor would not
expect too much from a four-and-a-half year old
boy, he saw a smiling Keith on his way to school.

In a way, he was glad that he would be taking
them. Jenny's new job at Pye's meant that she left
the house at 7.30 a.m., giving her little time to
prepare the kids for school. Also, Pimbo sometimes worked late into the evening, which meant
that he saw little of his children during the day.

Newmarket Road, between 8.30 and 9 a.m., was
one mass of traffic, so much so, that a policeman
was always on duty at the junction leading off into
East Road. Pimbo fell foul of him on his very first
morning taking the kids to school.

The errand-cycle, which Pimbo used for transport had a very high basket that he found very
practical for holding brushes and polish on delivery day. It also housed Christine and Keith very
neatly, making a cheap and easy means of transport – until the copper spotted them! "Hullo,
Hullo, what have we here? Two for the price of
one!" With a long trail of traffic behind him,
Pimbo sheepishly removed the two youngsters

from the basket. "Against the regulations!" chided the man in blue, as Pimbo began his long walk to the Shrubbery.

That was until, out of sight of the law, he quickly popped them into the basket again to finish the journey to school — but, trouble was still around the corner!

Turning into Hills Road from St Paul's Road, Pimbo spotted a line of expensive cars pulling in at the entrance to the Shrubbery School. All ready, smart, uniformed youngsters, with spanking new satchels made from real leather, were being shepherded into the school, by business-suited dads, and career-clad mums.

Pimbo looked down at the faces of Christine and Keith, they were blushing deep red! Instead of stopping at the school gates, he did a U-turn back into St Paul's Road. "I'm sorry, kids, we'll stop here. You can walk down to the school. Another day, traffic or no traffic, I'll bring the car. We'll ride slap bang up to the school, just like the others, how's about that, eh?"

"Thank's dad!" they replied in unison; as they walked away, Pimbo detected new spring in their step.

As he moved away from Hills Road, and on towards his working territory; Pimbo got to reckoning on his life, since leaving the army. There seemed to be more pressure than the pre-war days of looking forward to week-ends, pictures, football matches and so forth. With Jenny now at work, the kids starting private school, meant a relentless urge to earn more money.

It seemed that men coming straight from 'demob' were saying, "I've got to make it. I'm not going back to the thirties — I must get myself a regular job, provide a good home for my wife and kids — I know what my parents went through. Oh no, it's not for me!"

Then again, by the time Jenny got home from work, prepared the meals, tidied round, putting the kids to bed, topped up a very heavy day for her; there seemed to be very little time for real leisure. Pimbo, of course, helped where he could; getting the youngsters off in the mornings, gave him an inkling what mothers had to put up with when at home all day with the kids.

"I can't find my P.E. shoes", "Where's my satchel?", "What about my dinner-money?" Both Christine and Keith had their moments; each in turn, hid each other's school equipment, until, under dad's threat of making them walk to school, these priceless articles revealed themselves, under the stairs, under the cushions, or under the bedclothes.

Sometimes things became desperate, especially for Keith, who, on Jenny's tucking him in for the night, was found fully dressed, boots, cap, satchel, all worn, against the fear of not being able to find them in the morning!

As Pimbo was thinking; — there just didn't seem time for anything other than work. But, an old gentleman, later in the day, put him right on that score!

Mr Daynes, a widower of some years since, was a regular polish customer of Pimbo. "Like to keep the place nice, my missus would polish through every morning. 'Haven't got time to go out!' she'd say, 'I'm far too busy!' "

The old man looked up at his brush salesman. "But boy! I can give you a few years, you won't mind my calling you boy. I used to say to her, Gladys, my dear, when you're too busy, means one thing — you're *too* busy!"

Catching Pimbo's quizzical look, Mr Daynes sighed. "Yes, that's right, boy, you're *too* busy! If my wife were alive today, I'd see that she left the house more often, I'd take her for nice long walks — but, there you are, my boy, never get *too* busy. If you're wondering why I still polish, well it's just for memory's sake, and I don't do it every day!"

Pimbo smiled as he left the old fellow with his memories. A few doors away was a dear lady, Mrs Holliman, she was a Salvation Army follower, uniform and all. Each year, Pimbo would almost bet on which room she would be dusting out, so methodical she was, and a stickler for routine. However, this did not stop her inviting him in for a welcome cup of tea and biscuit. Over the usual table of refreshment, Mrs Holliman was looking across to Pimbo in a more than usual manner.

"I was thinking!" she said at length. "A little bird tells me that your two youngsters have started at the Shrubbery School — I was wondering if you ever stopped to think how the Lord has blessed you and your wife!"

Pimbo blinked. "How did you know?"

"Mrs White, she's a dear friend of mine. Helps at dinner-time, serves meals and washes up!" replied the good lady.

Pimbo recalled how Christine, when helping to wash-up, at the drying of the cutlery, would place

Pimbo takes his two children to school.

the lot into a dry tea-cloth, roll and rub away, until no hand manipulation was required. "That's how Mrs White does it, Dad!" Christine would say, proudly.

Well, do you count your blessings?" Mrs Holliman pushed home.

"We both work hard. But we're always aware that God has given us the opportunity — what are you getting at?"

"You have a persuasive tongue, I mean that kindly. The Lord could use you both in his work. The Shrubbery School is noted for its leaning towards a Christian upbringing for all its pupils — you could, kind of, keep up the continuity for your children?"

It suddenly dawned on Pimbo that today could be his day of reckoning! The kids, new spring in their step, their 'Thank you Dad!' Then too, there was Mr Daynes, with his little message, and now, Mrs Holliman.

He remembered too, his T.B. days. How he would pray that he would reach school-leaving age. From there he would pray for the maturity of 21, then, of course, the war years of praying for both he and Jenny. Everything had been answered! Now it was his turn, too, as Mrs Holliman suggests, to do something in return.

It wasn't being mawkish, he wouldn't care what people might think. He would talk to Jenny about it!

CHAPTER 12

Jenny At Work

Jenny was finding her job at Pye's, although at times a little irksome, quite rewarding in that it afforded her a chance to meet new friends. Her job was to spot-solder certain parts in a circuit, which, coming through on the assembly line, reminded her of Charlie Chaplin in 'Modern Times', although, thank goodness, she did not develop the tic that Charlie had in the film.

'Music while you work' was a feature of the factory floor, although at times it could be a little offsetting. Someone was always collecting at break-time for girls who would be leaving to 'get married'. This procedure, however, was eventually stopped, mainly because within six months or so, the recipient of the present would be back at work, having found that her wage was a vital factor towards running a home. Gossip was, of course, rampant with so many women together. At times Jenny wondered whether *anyone* escaped the wagging tongues. If three women were standing together, one would be thinking of the other, 'I wish she'd go, because I want to talk about her'!

Many of the women lived in Ditton Fields, and had been working for years at the factory. Always was a nagging fear of being 'stood off'. Rumours that contracts were either lost, or mammoth ones gained, kept the girls at concert pitch. Jenny found the money a buffer against anything that the children might require for school, also, it made her feel proud that she, as well as Pimbo, was contributing towards keeping the children at the Shrubbery.

On that particular Monday, Jenny was off with a slight chill. She found the company of Mr Nunn, a relief from the sense of isolation she had found with almost everyone in the area at work. Mr Nunn was the Co-op rep. who came round on Mondays in order to take Jenny's list of grocery requirements. The order usually came to around thirty shillings, which stocked her up until the ensuing Thursday, when the order was delivered by the Co-op van. Bill lived in Stansfield Road on the opposite estate. An ex-RAF man, he and Pimbo swapped yarns about their war-time experiences.

"I'm afraid this might be my last week for taking orders!" Bill was saying, over a cup of tea with Jenny in the kitchen. "The Co-op's not making it pay, there's rumours of the Newmarket Road branch closing down. It could mean I'm for the chop — !"

Jenny pushed across a second cup of tea. "What will you do, Mr Nunn, anything in line?"

Bill grinned. "I've been with them for many years. I'm sure they'll find me something behind the counter. I suppose really I could see it coming. There's so little profit on groceries, what with the big stores opening up. Then, too, the Co-op are losing some of their transport, they've started hiring vans — that takes away a good deal of profit!"

At that moment, Pimbo walked in.

After he had been put in the picture by Jenny, Pimbo turned to Bill Nunn. "Are the Union fighting for you, you've told me so much about the merits of your Union?"

Closing his order book, the grocery rep. smiled up at his mocker. "They can't do much about the closure of the Newmarket Road branch. You see, they're opening new branches all over the country, the staff have the option of moving into the new jobs, 'picking up sticks' if you see what I mean. But, what about you? Time you moved into the political scene, bright young man straight from the Army, what about joining our party — you've had experience in both management and rank-and-file?"

Pimbo smiled. He remembered that during the war, despite Churchill's popularity as a leader in war, his political prowess had been severely damaged. During lulls in fighting, men had more time to think. A report that Churchill's lodge keepers had been paid pitiful wages had swept through the ranks. The great man's life style was considered as a mockery against the man and wife's poor quality of living on peanut wages. Pimbo reckoned that the ordinary man with a gun in his hand was saying, 'I'm doing my bit, Mr Churchill, now when this shin-dig's over — do something for me!' It was the first time that the working man had a chance to hit back. As one squaddy was heard to say, 'He spends more on cigars in a day than his lodge-keepers' month wages!' It may have been a great surprise to many at Churchill's election defeat — but the majority of Desert Rats *knew* it was coming!

"Well?" asked a patient Bill Nunn.

"I'm really not a political man, Bill. My idea of a *good* Government is one that embraces everyone; rich, poor, ailing, young and old, schools, hospitals, you name them. You take *what* makes a good officer, in my book, it's the fellow who looks after the men. He can go to the Officer's Mess, Officer's Ball, the Officer's re-union dinner, but unless he's looked after his men, he won't go with a clear conscience!

"But some do!" butted in Bill. "Some don't care about the men. They come straight from Sandhurst, they don't understand about real issues. We get them in politics, that's where *you* come in, you've been through the lot, you can say your piece!"

Pimbo nodded. He thought about Lt. Armstrong, straight from Officers Training Corps. He gave orders right, left and centre. He used the men as robots; they might miss time for writing letters home, miss a little welcome kip, but Lt. Armstrong, after a gruelling session, would stride away to the comfort of the Officer's Mess, saying to Pimbo, "Right. Carry on, Sergeant!"

One day, after a growing resentment from the men, Lt. Armstrong placed his hand on Pimbo's shoulder. "You tell them, Sergeant. You tell them, they understand you, you're one of them!"

The Officer was only nineteen, he'd been to Marlborough Public School. But he was willing to learn — and learn he did, turning into a grand officer, who always put his men first. Pimbo vowed, if he ever went into politics — Pimbo would join his party!

Jenny, who had been listening to the men's conversation, suddenly entered the kitchen. "I want my man to do something for his family. My old dad went through both wars, finished up with nothing to his name. A member of the British Legion, swapping yarns over half-a-pint of beer, that's how he finished; they had to collect round to bury him. Had he been killed in war, at least he'd have been buried for nothing!"

Pimbo smiled at Jenny's logic. That morning, he had been listening to a similar story from Mr Marshall, who had been telling of his dad's having been at Mons, then enlisting for the Second World War, and what's more, seeing service right up to the end! 'William-the-Conqueror,' Pimbo had named him!

Bill Nunn was getting a trifle impatient. "This is a long way from my round's closing. I don't expect you to rush out and buy a 'Karl Marx' — give it thought. You don't have to be a 'Red' in order to get your views expressed!"

The engrossed trio, realising the intensity of their talk, broke up into a gale of laughter, leaving the young married couple on their own.

After Bill had gone, Jenny tackled Pimbo on his political persuasions. Jenny had heard so much of her parent's bickerings over what sort of Government should preside; it seemed that they each had their own particular party.

Pimbo looked thoughtful. "I feel, sometimes, too much store is placed on personality. This clouds over the real issues; look at it like this — suppose the country was a sinking ship, the captain would order 'Abandon Ship'. Well, one party, I'll leave you to guess who, would probably, put up life-belts, for sale — only people with money could save themselves! The other party would try to see that everyone had access to the life-belts. Lives would be lost, of course, but propaganda would see to it that little credit be given to the free-for-all policy — instead, the captain putting life-belts for sale would be praised for raising the money (through sale of life-belts), to purchase another ship!"

Jenny laughed at Pimbo's simple analogy. "I think it's high time that we got ourselves involved in some kind of work for the church. What with Unions, politics and what have you, we'll never make our mark in any of those — !"

Barnwell Baptist Church was a new church, springing up from a little hut in Ditton Fields. In a few homes in the Fields, Sunday School was held in the front parlours. Such stalwarts as the Saunders, George, Mason and Boundy, were pioneers, helping to spread the gospel among the working-class areas. Following closely on the heels of their talk with Bill Nunn, and Jenny's proposition concerning joining a church — the Unwin's found themselves as new church members.

A fiery little Welshman, the Rev. E. H. Bowen,

was Barnwell's very first paid minister. He lodged a fair distance from the church, (in Victoria Road) due to the close proximity of the Unwin's home in Keynes Road, Mr Bowen, to Jenny's delight, often popped in for a cup of tea and chat.

He was telling Jenny, one afternoon, about his brother being in the Navy, and a niece of his, who apparently, suffered from a form of epilepsy. True to the Welsh tradition for learning, Mr Bowen told of his niece being admonished for bad behaviour by a scornful, "All right, then, you won't go to Gerty's!" — Gertie's being slang for Girton College.

Mr Bowen was immediately dubbed 'Vic' by the Unwins. Church expenses during the winter far outweighed the meagre collection on Sunday. Vic was a familiar figure in the church vicinity, wheeling a small woman's cycle, with a large can of paraffin balanced on the handle-bars, sometimes he made the journey from his lodgings, almost 2½ miles away, in order to supplement the church's heating expenses.

In the evenings, Pimbo and Jenny would listen to Vic, as he unfolded a string of tales, which, not always, put the church in a good light. "You see!" he would explain, "The reason people don't come to church is because they think they're not good enough, but believe me, we're not all saints inside — we, at times, need church more than they do!"

During the day, when the church did not require several paraffin stoves firing on all cylinders, Vic could be seen foraging among the second-hand bookshops in town. Davids, in Sennitt's Passage, was among his regular calls. On

returning to the Unwins in the evening, Mr
Bowen would present Pimbo with a rare discovery
he'd unearthed for a mere shilling. 'Thomas Kem-
pis', 'Imitation of Christ', 'Pilgrim's Progress',
'Tom Sawyer', all bound volumes, came within his
scope.

Through Vic, Jenny had discovered the depth
and beauty of 'Little Women'. She was keeping in
store for Christine the moment when Jo, the
extrovert daughter, had asked her mother, 'Will
you force me to marry someone with money?' and
mum's reply, 'only if you love him, I want you to be
happy, decent, and to bring up your children in
like manner — of course, should you be rich as
well — that, my girl, would be an extra bonus!'

Sometimes Jenny feared for her children's future. In 'Little Women', life seemed so differerent.
Every day was an adventure, something new, was
a traumatic event. Parties, in those days, were
real parties, the children did their own little
'party piece'. Now, it was telly, and the host party,
boy, or girl, would snatch away the formal present
from the little hands of the invited guest. Pimbo
would say, 'it all sounds better in books'.

Barnwell Baptist church was growing. Miss
Cox, through her Campaigners, had brought in
many young girls, the elder of these such as; Ida
Raiment, Sylvia Tombs, Jean Noble — had infiltrated into the Sunday School teaching classes,
thus building up a nucleus of youth for the future.

Stalwarts — Albert Saunders, his wife, Doris
Wilson and husband, Mr Ingle, and the devoted
couple Mr and Mrs Parkinson, had seen the
church through its birth-pangs, and now enjoyed

the 'bonny bouncing baptists babes' coming into the future of the church.

As Vic was saying, "Now, it's up to you, why not become officers of the Campaigners, start a boys' group? The church is very short of boys, Mr Saunders and Mr Parkinson are getting older and we need new blood!"

Jenny had relished Vic's coming into the church, and into her life. Every Friday, on pay day, she would collect Christine from school, to take her into Woolworth's, where pocket editions of 'Heidi' and 'Little Women' could be purchased for half-a-crown; she wanted her daughter brought up into good literature, it was through Vic, and his second-hand bookshop meanderings, that had brought about such desire!

Pimbo, in turn, had received similar benefits from Vic's advent into the Unwin's household. Although, ever a keen reader, most of the classics; Dickens, Ballytine, Defoe, had been read by him during his T.B. convalescence. But the 'Dictionary of National Biography' whereby all the great men of the past had been indexed, listed and pen pictured, was a great innovation into the book world, coupled with Rogets Theseraus, both obtained by Vic from 'Davids' at a shilling apiece, cloth bound at that, were priceless gems, one day, thought Pimbo, he would write a book!

Mr Bowen was a batchelor, coming from a poor Welsh mining village. As in 'How Green is my Valley', Vic had dedicated himself into learning, becoming a Minister was his sole longing, at the expense of marriage and a loving relationship with the opposite sex.

The Rev. E. H. Bowen brings in yet another book.

Sometimes, both Jenny and Pimbo thought of Vic's treating them as though they were his own children, for them, he sought the best, and through literature, he was able to open a new window on to the world!

But, Vic's keen Welsh humour cast aside any morbid reckonings. It was this which had induced Pimbo and Jenny to set out on new adventures by becoming Campaigner Officers, to start off an influx of boys into the Barnwell Church!

CHAPTER 13

The Job Lot

Jenny was finding work at Pye's rather tedious. The same faces, same routine, and never a hope of a pay-rise, was beginning to take its toll. A job as shop assistant at Grantchester House in Regent Street, which served both as a post office, and toy-shop was taken by Jenny.

The journey by bus, meeting fresh faces daily, and being able to take lunch at a small nearby cheerful cafe, gave Jenny the change she needed. The work too, was light and fulfilling. Children, testing out new toys, with anxious parents watching with loving eyes, as their offspring shrieked with delight at the new toy trends, which had come into being, as rationing and utility furniture had been given the order of the boot!

Lovely coloured rocking horses, beautiful dolls with dresses to match; for the boys — tanks and soldiers, all in colour, Jenny smiled as she watched young lads try out the guns with a clicking of teeth in mimicry of a gun-shot. With a long terrible war slowly receding from memory, the toy makers seemed to be preparing young blood for World War Three — would they ever learn? — thought Jenny.

This brought her mind to Christine. With rationing now over, things were getting more plentiful in the shops. utility clothing, once drab and shapless, now bright and attractive, shoes in more colourful trends, were the order of the day. Indeed, things were looking up — after work, Jenny had arranged to pick up her daughter from the Shrubbery, in order to buy her a new skirt and shoes.

Robert Sayle's was the venue for the shopping excursion, Jenny had saved for the occasion, and a small bonus from her toy-selling achievements had topped up the money presumably required. Christine was growing up into a lovely young girl, and was just beginning to find her feet on life's rocky pathway!

Jenny had always chosen Christine's attire, money shortage had governed the type of dress or coat. Had it room for a turning-up? Did it allow for growth? Would it wash well? Usually, the utility fashions spoke for themselves. It was, take it — or leave it! But, today was going to be different, Jenny found to her cost!

First the shoes! Christine turned down all the flat-heeled, broad fitting ones. Little Miss Junior, was the vogue! "All the girls at the Shrubbery are wearing them, Mum!" pointed out Christine. "I like this pair, half-way heels, strap over, you see, Mum, things are different now. Don't forget, I'm eleven now!"

Catching the eye of the assistant, Jenny frowned. This was the very first time that her daughter had ever questioned her ability to choose the correct attire for her. Jenny was thinking of her Orphanage days — then, dresses, coats and shoes, came in bundles, no choice at all, the kids just rectified any bad fittings among themselves.

The assistant broke her thoughts. "This pair, I think, Madam, very fashionable, we sell a lot of these. We have them in other colours, but your daughter seems to have settled for the brown!" Now it was the skirt! Pleated, straight, tartan, braced, belted, or elastic waisted. Christine turned all Jenny's choices down emphatically.

"It's no good, Mum! I want a flared skirt, the straight ones are 'old hat'!" Tucking the assistant's proffered flared style close to her waist, Christine did a twirl. "You see what I mean, Mum? It's the new thing in — !"

"Don't tell me!" snapped an impatient Jenny. "All the girls are wearing them at the Shrubbery, I don't suppose straight, ordinary skirts will ever come back again!"

Christine gave her mum a hug. "You want me to do well at school — don't you, Mum? The girls will laugh at me if I don't wear trendy things — I promise that I'll take care of my new things!"

Paying over the money, Jenny was thinking of Jill Thomas, a girl of Christine's age, who, also, was a pupil at the Shrubbery. Jill lived in Egerton Close, close to Keynes Road. It seemed that the girl was from a well-to-do family; Digby Wolfe, a well known actor, was an uncle of Jill's. Jenny realised that keeping up to Jill Thomas' life style wasn't going to be easy — in fact, she wasn't even going to try!

Coming out of Sayle's, Jenny took in the scene.

Almost opposite, was the spot where Sluice Parker had been involved in a fatal accident. The new Post Office stood out against the older buildings. Miller's had gone from the corner of Hobson Street, to take up a position further along — later, of course, to disappear altogether.

Since the war, things were moving. Shops were changing hands, new innovations of retail service were mushrooming. One thing, though, Jenny felt – that apart from the big stores, customer service wasn't up to pre-war standards. She remembered Coad's, attentive assistants, a chair always available for tired feet. Now, Coad's had gone, maybe taking with it all the good things. She smiled, as she remembered taking her change in the form of a packet of pins.

Christine was getting impatient, she wanted to get home to try on her new things. Jenny wondered how her son Keith would react to his sister's new purchases. A few days ago, Pimbo had been caught in the new fashion's web. Spotting a youth's overcoat in a Smart's of Market Street sale; going for a pound, he couldn't get home quick enough to present it to his son. It was of blue melton-cloth, a real beauty! Pimbo watched his son's face as he tried on the overcoat.

Keith's face grew longer and longer, not a sign of appreciation to be seen on his pink youthful countenance.

"What's wrong?" asked his dad in complete innocence.

"It's too long, Dad. The boys will laugh at me. Overcoats, nowadays, are just knee-length, this comes down to my ankles. Dad — you've got to get with it!"

Now, it had been Jenny's turn to get with it! Bringing up a family wasn't getting easier, thought Jenny. As Christine grew older, it was going to be boy friends, late parties, and yet more trendy clothes. Jenny was thinking of her mother's warnings. "Wait until you have children of your own, my girl, you won't think I'm too strict, then, mark my words — my gal!"

Jenny smiled at the thought of a conversation she'd overheard on the bus. A girl of eighteen was telling her contemporary, "My dad nearly drove my first boyfriend away. He'd brought me to the back door; my dad bellowed at him, — 'What time do you call this — ?' — It was only nine-thirty! I nearly died when my boyfriend pointed out that we'd only come back for me to powder up, he was thinking of taking me to a dance!"

Going along Newmarket Road, the bus, with its many stops, gave Jenny a chance to see all the changes which had taken place since her childhood days. Gone was Gray's pet shop accessories. Jack Reynolds, unlike brother Tim, was still reigning supreme with his little shop which catered for so many things a hurried shopper might forget. The cycle shop of Frost's, had moved from its East Road corner site, but prevailed still, next to Jack's place.

J. Gray, the sweet and tobacconist, surprisingly, had held its own against allcomers. Jenny loved to see the old fashioned sweet jars, militant like, paraded in his shop window. Hutchison's Court, now gone — the most infamous of Cambridge yards. No boy dare enter its bowels, should one dare, they had the rats of the Corporation refuse pit to contend with. Pimbo had said that Hutchison's Court would make the present Gorbals seem like a Nun's cloister!

Traylen's had lost out a little, space-wise, but in keeping with the new style of deep-freeze and butchery, was making do — thank you very much! Cook's cycle repair garage was on the way out, new type motor cycles had pushed through like sprouting bulbs in spring. Jenny smiled at a memory of the old gentleman that was in charge of repairs. A young go-getter, with his new motor-scooter, had gone in for a puncture repair. The old chap who had been with Cook's for many years, and must have done hundreds of cycle puncture repairs, looked anxiously down at the punctured rear-wheel. "Well, boy, if I can get the wheel out – I'll have a go at it!"

Times indeed were changing! Jenny watched Christine's face, as proudly, she hung on the Robert Sayle's carrier bag with all her new trendy things. The bus was getting crowded, passengers were on and off at every stop. A small group of women shoppers dumped themselves down at the rear of the bus, Jenny recognised them as people from her estate; having got on at the rear of the bus they had not yet caught sight of Jenny.

"I see her out shopping with that girl of hers!" one woman was saying. "Fancy's herself a bit, since she got her girl into the Shrubbery — next thing, she'll be moving somewhere more classy!"

"She can only go where the Council send her — unless she actually buys her own house!" put in another.

Jenny sat frozen as the talk went on.

"What's it to do with us? Don't blame her trying for the best for her kids. A few more could do the same if they didn't spend so much in the pubs — half the women only go out to work because their old man keeps them short — good luck to her, I says!"

Jenny could almost have kissed the last speaker.

The bus reached its terminal point. Jenny, deliberately, was the last to get off, having a full vision of the gossiping women, who, on spotting Jenny, with red faces, mumbled some kind of greeting.

Jenny's advocate was trotting behind as the group made their various ways home. "Thank you, my dear!" said Jenny. "Nice to know that someone understands. I'll bet you had a good reason for sticking up for me?"

"Mrs Stocker, I'm Mrs Stocker, only moved in a few months ago, I often see your two on the bus, bonny kids they are, too. Come in for a cup of tea, rest your legs, my dear!"

The elderly lady moved across to the little bungalows in Ekin Road. With the tea cups rattling, Mrs Stocker looked across at Jenny, who was sampling the nice cosy kitchen, the warmth of the red curtains, and the home-made rugs. "Yes, my dear, I lost my husband a year ago, but really it was my son who prompted my little foray for you on the bus!"

Pouring out the tea, the old lady went on. "My son has gone, too, killed in the war; but, one of his school-boy friends got a scholarship to the Perse.

Jack, that's my son, often used to say how he wished that he, too, could have gone to a better school — but, things worked out differently!"

Noticing tears welling into the corner of Mrs Stocker's eyes, Jenny turned to Christine, who was admiring the old lady's budgie. "You'd best be getting along, Chris, you can be trying on your new gear, but don't start any arguments with Keith!"

Mrs Stocker had dried her eyes. "After I lost Jack, I used to punish myself for not pushing him harder at school. But, life's funny. The Perse schoolboy went through the war without a scratch, got himself a good job in a solicitor's ofice. I used to catch sight of him, sitting at the window, real proud like — !"

"And, then?" put in Jenny.

"I was reading the local paper, one night. There was his name, on a charge of embezzlement. He got a three years sentence. I used to say to myself, my Jack wouldn't have done that — so you see, that's why I stuck up for you on the bus. Give your kids a chance, I say, but people don't understand — jealousy, I'd say!"

On her way out, Jenny looked across at the other bungalows, similar to Mrs Stocker's. One spouse or other was missing from each household. The old lady, struggling in the garden, or the old gentleman trying his hand at the washing. She smiled as she noticed one old fellow tossing a wet sheet over the line. Her mum had taught her to peg on a sheet so that it could billow, and let the air get through.

Then, too, her mum had taught her to always

put your best linen in the centre of the line. Hang
the dicy bits closer to the house — prying neighbours couldn't spot them so easily. Her mum had
told how a neighbour had borrowed someone's
best linen to hang on *her* line; so as to impress a
relative coming down from the North on a day's
visit!

Mrs Stocker was waving goodbye, as Jenny
passed the corner leading into Keynes Road. Mrs
Boundy, standing at her gate, reminded Jenny of
a Young Wives meeting that night. A real pillar of
Barnwall Church was Mrs Boundy, with her son,
Ian, ready to follow suit.

Arriving home, Jenny found Christine looking
smart and proud in her new outfit. "Thanks,
Mum, one day I'll repay you for all you do — the
girls will love this, can I go out in them tonight,
Mum?"

Jenny smiled to herself. So far, it was 'the girls
will love this', soon it was going to be 'the boys'.
She was steeling herself for that day, but it would
have to come. Jenny and Pimbo had always kept a
firmish rein on the kids. After seven at night,
being on the streets was taboo! A bath, hot milk
drink, and a fifteen minute look at the telly —
then bed.

Of course, there were the whisperings on the
landings, then the final, "Can we come down,
Mum?" All in all, however, the kids felt more
secure through discipline.

When Pimbo came in, his first thoughts were
concerning Jenny's job at Grantchester House.
With giggles and at times more serious thought,
they came to the conclusion that bus fares, mid-

*"It's no good, Mum. I want a flared skirt!" said
Christine firmly.*

day lunch, and the little toy cars that Jenny
purchased each week, ate into her wage to such an
extent, that very little money was left over to
justify a week's toil!

Pimbo, next day received good news concerning
his own job — he was offered the position of

manager at the new Harlow town. Taking the
position would involve moving house, raising a
sales force from scratch, and, of course, estab-
lishing his own selling round. Finding accommodation and removal expenses were left to Pimbo's own resources. Despite a letter sent to Betterwear's H.Q., they remained firm on those issues.

The children's having to find a new school and
friends became the turning point! — they would
stay as they were! As Jenny pointed out "Betterwear's make sure that they take no chances! Then
too, the ladies on the bus would take none too
kindly to our moving house — proper snobs,
they'd call us!"

THE HAPPIEST LAND

They sat one day in quiet,
In a pub known as The Plough.
Which stood beside the river,
Near Grassy Corner's brow!

The landlord topped their glasses;
Around the old dart-board.
Then, sat they all, so calm and still,
With never a hasty word!

But when mine host departed,
A Ditton-man raised his hand;
And cried, all hot, and flushed with beer;
"Long Live Fen-Ditton's Land!"

"The greatest village in Cambridgeshire,
Cannot with Ditton compare;
With all those fit young rowing men,
And the sweetest damsels there!"

"Ha!" cried a Quy-man laughing
And splashing his beard with wine;
"I'd rather live in dear old Quy,
Than that Ditton place of thine!"

"It's the finest place in all the Land,
And has most fertile soil,
The buxom ladies toil the fields,
And their off-springs, do not spoil!"

"Hold your tongues — both Ditton and Quy!"
A Bottisham yokel cries.
"If there's a heaven upon this earth —
In Bot'sam, *there*, it lies!"

"There, the race-course stands nearby,
And the farmer grows fine corn.
The Autumn hedges, flaming hue,
Matches the Sun at dawn!"

The listening Landlord smiled,
Up to heaven, raised his hand.
And said, "No more need ye contend —
There, lies the Happiest Land!"

Fred Unwin

CHAPTER 14

Sport in Cambridge

Keith, sport wise, was following in his father's footsteps. Pimbo, in his earlier days had played for several local clubs; Arthurians, St Georges (not the school), Fitzroy Thursday, Camden (1st and 2nds). Having had a trial for Iliston FC, he was able to play only once through the war's intervention, but, to his delight, guested for Cambridge United, then known as Abbey United, during a spell of home leave.

Keith was now going to the Manor School; true to to his parents planning, he was to leave the Shrubbery on reaching secondary school age. To Pimbo's pleasure, Keith had turned out to be a good chess player, but, apart from reaching chess club standard, his heart lay in soccer.

In true fatherly fashion, Pimbo journeyed up to Manor School playing fields, to watch for the first time, his son playing in an important inter-schools match. During the course of light-hearted banter, Pimbo had got the impression that Keith had not always enjoyed a first team choice. It seemed that his son adopted a similar style to that of his dad, one of taking on opposing backs, and dribbling through into the penalty area.

Maybe shouts of 'Get rid of it' as soon as Keith was given the ball, was the answer to his irregular appearances. But, that day, Keith gave them their money's worth. Beside scoring a great goal, he made one other through a thrusting run, at half time his side was leading by three clear goals — then came the crunch!

"We'll hang on to our three goals lead! Drop back in defence, boys, and the match is ours!" was the order of the team coach.

During the half-time period, Pimbo looked round at the doting parents. Many, no doubt, had visions of their offspring reaching the dizzy heights of professional status — even International class! "If only my boy had a bit more weight!" "He's got the speed, if only he can remember to take the ball with him!" "He's not cut out for all that rough stuff!" a mother would chip in. "I wish I had my time over again, these kids have got it made, they ought to try heading a *real* ball on a muddy day — blimey, the lace would cut 'em to bits!" finished a disgruntled father.

Pimbo recognised a few of the speakers. Alby Ellis, the old St George's boy. Dave Wallace, the Thursday Wanderers hero. Ron Hickman, the ex-Beehive wizard. The Stocker brothers, referee and player respectively. Each had filled out into the dreaded middle-aged spread, which had showed in the pre-match kick-about, that the heart was willing, but the old muscles would not respond!

Jack Chapman, the ex-City player and math's teacher, was in charge of the boys soccer training.

Keith had often told Pimbo of the trainer's love and dedication to the game. Pimbo's doubts about going on the defence to hold on to a three goal lead, were proved correct. The opposition, launching an all out attack, finished up as winners by the goal of seven — 4–3.

Several boys had shown real potential — Roger Staden, John Circuit, Alan Wolfe. Pimbo was very pleased with his boy's showing. "A chip off the old block, eh, Keith. You just keep playing your own game — there's too much of 'Get rid of it'! Kick and rush football — we need someone capable of holding the ball and taking 'em on. Mind you, don't overdo the fancy stuff — just read the game!"

Keith smiled at his dad's little meanderings into the halcyon days of his youth. Midsummer Common on a Sunday morning would be full of aspiring footballers, teams of twenty-a-side would play from 10 a.m. until 2 p.m. non-stop — apart from changing ends. Coats, as goalposts? — Anyone having to leave early would shout, "Put your coat down, Dave, I'm off!"

Scores such as thirty-thirty would merit the old cry, "Winning goal and quit!" Such was the frenzy, Pimbo recalled, that a winning goal might take yet another hour to decide.

Arguments in plenty buzzed around whether the ball going over the top of a coat, 'was in, or hitting a post'. Then, too, the height of a ball going over the goalie's head, again was debatable. "It would have hit the bar!" usually became a sensible ploy to enable the game to go on.

Eddie Collins, Harold Barker, Sammy Corn-

wall, Ernie Caldicoat, all at one time had received
their baptism at the crude and punishing 6 hours
combats, to go on to become City players, as had
Dick Harris, Dusty Clements, Curly Smart, and
'good old' Harvey Cornwall; likewise followed into
the Abbey United Camp. Of the younger set, Titch
Thurston, Cherry Palmer, Harry Witt, the
Richardson brothers, graced local soccer for many
years.

Sport in Cambridge, thought Pimbo, since the
war, had gradually deteriorated. Pre-war on
Thursday afternooons, great throngs of spectators
would line the side-lines, and several matches
would be on the go. A special Thursday League,
complete with its Shield and Cup, made sure of
keen competition. Teams from as far away as
Saffron Walden, with its crack little team, Saffron
Walden Lillies, competed in these Corinthian type
matches, where, actually *enjoying* the game, took
precedence over dirty play, and foul language.

Pimbo remembered a Saturday match at the
Abbey Stadium a few weeks ago, he had been
thinking about his pre-war days of football,
where, during the week, his whole mind seemed
to be awaiting the match he would be playing in.
The teams were running on to the pitch, and
Pimbo felt envious of the fit, bronzed-looking men,
who would be displaying their skills in front of
thousands of spectators. Within a minute of play,
a vicious foul, had stretchered off one player, with
the ref. sending off the fouling culprit. Pimbo
couldn't understand why a player could wait all
week for a game, then, *intentionally* jeapardise
his chances of playing the full ninety minutes.

Awaiting his son's appearance from the dressing room, Pimbo was chatting with Mr Segrave, the removal's tycoon. "I'm starting a Sunday Youth team!" he was saying, "I like your lad's style, not afraid to take on the defence — would you care to let him join?"

Pimbo nodded in assent. Parents, he thought, should back up their children in any venture which could lead to their staying out of trouble. Strange it was that some fathers neglected this wise adage. Perhaps, not being sport loving themselves, restricted their vision of a healthy outlet for their offspring. Aside from any sporting aspect, he remembered a neighbour whose son was to collect his CSE certificate from an open-day event at school.

His mother begged Pimbo to attend, acting as a stand-in for the boy's father. "Bert's got a special darts match on — besides, you have a job to get him to go anywhere — I didn't think *you'd* mind!"

Of course, on the other hand, you could take sport a bit too far! It might interfere with your courting prowess, as Pimbo once found out to his cost! Most of his spare time was spent on the playing field, winter or summer — girls never came into his reckoning. However, a young lady with a crush on him managed at last to tie him down with a date!

So, where Pimbo would usually be found at cricket on the Gilbert Road housing site, here was he, arm-in-arm, with this maiden fair, on a fine Sunday afternoon; where the plob of bat against ball, could be heard as he passed by his micky-taking friends!

Add to this, a long walk from one end of the town to the other, pushing a wheel-chair with a heavy, cynical girl's mum, then, you have the ingredients for producing a mixed-up, less than love-lorn, swain!

Pimbo torn between his love of sport, and a repeat of his first courtship, threw in the towel in favour of sport — courting would have to wait!

Keith's last year at the Manor School saw him blossoming out as a cricketer as well as as competent soccer player — ripe for joining a local club. For many boys, the last year at school became a boring, time-wasting period. Most were anxious to start work, and unless academically gifted, found those final months as irksome as a mother-to-be awaiting her first child — a little absenteeism was used as a cushion against such problems!

Ron Morgan, in his capacity of school-board-man, was telling Pimbo of his experience when visiting a particularly constant offender! A 'headache' on Friday gave the boy a nice long week-end from school. Over a cup of tea in the kitchen, Ron was taking this point up with the apologetic father.

"Well, you can't blame him really, you know!" the father was saying. "The Eleven Plus lark is enough to break any boy's heart — thrown on the scrap heap, I'd say!"

Ron, as he was sinking a second cup of tea, nodded. "My lad plays for the same team as your boy; Seagrave's Sunday Eleven, eh? Never misses a game, fully recovered by Saturday for team practice — then, on Sunday, for the big game. There's me, a school-board-man, with a son playing the same tricks which *I'm* supposed to be checking up on!"

"You mean?" gasped a surprised Pimbo.

Ron laughed. "Don't let it go any further. It happens in every household — one way or another. One thing, I'd rather see them playing hookey for sport, than other reasons. I'd like to see some kind of scheme for a boy's last year at the Manor, like actually joining a firm for a year's apprenticeship!"

Pimbo got to thinking about sport in general; what it did for youngsters from the poorer homes. He thought back on Albie Chapman, during the week an errand boy at Bowes & Bowes. On Thursday afternoon, Albie, with his girl friend holding his arm, would trot on to Jesus Green, and within minutes, by dint of sterling work as left-back, he would become a somebody in his girl's eyes, plus a good report in the weekly sports page!

Cricket wise, we had Ted Doggett, Johnny Harris, Boxer Smith, 'Dids' Newman and Bill Mansfield, each holding a prominent position in the eyes of the Parker's Piece patrons. Freddy Bloy, getting together youth teams for the future — a real trouper! The Hudson's, Capitains, Pomeroys, Prime, with Geoff Mace sending down 'chinamen' as good as the next, and dear old Bill Ives astounding everybody! The swimming section gave us Jack Overhill, Dummy Barker, and little Charlie Driver, swimmer, custodian and life-saver supreme! For boxing, we had 'Buttons' Taylor — the brothers, Harry and Fred Toates, and dear old Gammy Smith.

"You're day-dreaming, Dad!" said Keith, as he met his dad outside the pavilion. "You look miles away! — What did you think of the game?"

Pimbo smiled. "You did well, boy. Good foot-work, you're better built than your old dad — you can move faster, but I think you should have played more times for the school — but, that's how it goes!"

Since the war, many faces were missing from the playing fields of Cambridge, the war had taken its toll. Dennis Imber, a promising young player, Diddles Thurlbourne, Harold Cobbold, H. Wilkin, the old Fitzroy goalie, those not killed had been swept into the domestic scene by marrying and taking on the responsibility of bring up a family.

Sport, in the pre-war days, had been a great therapeutic agent, to be used against unemploy-ment, poverty, and a leveller of class-distinction. Clad in white flannels, sweater, cricket boots, and a sweat band, one felt as good as another. Pimbo had in mind a fellow called Gill, by no means a great cricketer, but he always turned out in im-maculate style. Pimbo would view him with more than a little envy. It was almost a challenge. So it was down to George Dennington at the corner of St John's Street, after a good rummage among George's second-hand sports clothes, Pimbo emerged as a well-turned out cricketer, for the lost cost of five shillings!

The quality of play among the working class was, indeed, no substitute for their enthusiastic attitude to the game. Pimbo remembered a fellow called Brown, who, as captain, was a perfect example of the 'play up, play up, and play the game' breed of pre-war players.

His bowling was the type that 'came in' on the fourth bounce. Batsmen would literally murder him, but usually, with their score in the nineties, they would endeavour to hit Brown out of sight, to fall from a catch on the boundary. Runs *against* his bowling, meant nothing to Brown; "I knew I'd, get him in the end!" he would proudly say. A captured wicket, in the captains book, was the real crunch, as an angler might 'work in' a belated catch!

Fellowship House, a club run by students, was responsible for the re-habilitation of hundreds of young lads in Cambridge, who may well have used their energy in less healthy ways than cricket or football.

Arriving home, Pimbo and Keith found Jenny had received a visitor, it was Mr Bowen!

The 'Vic' seemed a little downcast. Over a cup of tea, the little minister put it to the young couple. "It seems that the church are after my blood — they want me out. I can't think what it is all about — but we shall have to make a fight of it!"

"Make a fight — what do you mean?" asked Jenny.

Mr Bowen shrugged. "You can petition for me, get a few names, I have many friends. You see, our sister church, St Andrews, is responsible for financing our stay here — without them, we would have to close down. The Diaconate, a set of Deacons, maybe see a fuller church with a new Minister. Mr Jestice, the present minister at St Andrews, is a grand fellow, we get on well, but,

Keith, finished off a lovely move — with his first goal!

I'm afraid as in politics, dealings are decided behind closed doors!"

"Will there be a vote taken?" asked an anxious Pimbo, who, at that moment, was thinking of Vic, trudging the length of Cambridge, with a large can of paraffin at the ready! Maybe, like Samuel in the Temple, perhaps Mr Bowen, with his chores of keeping the church warm, was preparing the place for one of higher esteem.

"There'll be a general meeting at St Andrew's, the Barnwell congregation will be welcomed. A decision will be made as to my future. As you ask

— yes, a vote will be taken, but, somehow, I feel God is calling me to another ministry — I must thank you for allowing me into your home — God bless you both!"

CHAPTER 15

Mr Bowen Departs

After many meetings, a few heated words, and sighs of regret from the Keynes Estate parishioners, the Reverend E. H. Bowen took his departure from the little Baptist church in Howard Road; in his place, came Mr P. Withers, a young man fresh from Spurgeon's wing, with the customary M.A. B.D. so befitting Baptist ministers.

The little church gradually grew; Saturday morning films, a Campaigner clan for girls under the able guidance of Margaret Cox as Chief, and Miss Chewter as her deputy, gave substance to the number of youth in the church. As Jenny was saying to Pimbo. "What about us starting a boys' clan. It would bring more lads into the church; besides, it would be a means of paying back Mr Bowen for all he has done for us?"

Pimbo nodded in agreement. There were lots of young lads around the estate, and plenty of mothers willing to get their lads off the streets! Mr and Mrs Twigwell were among the first to allow both John and Jean, their children, to join. The Twigwell's were exceptionally loving parents. Mrs Twigwell, a tiny little woman, worked very

hard as a domestic cleaner in order to get the very
best for their children. The husband, Bill, a suffer-
er of high blood pressure, worked at Marshall's.
John and Jean were rather boisterous youngsters,
giving their parents a hectic time. Bill, at times,
seemed to be a little bewildered by it all, but such
was their love for the children, the family lived
happily on an even keel.

Then too, was the Pilbeam family. Living
almost opposite the church, the parents with two
children, John and Mary; were delighted to allow
John to join his sister, who already, was in the
campaigners, John, a sturdy little blond-haired
lad, became one of Pimbo's staunchest Juno's.
Ever neatly attired in his uniform of blue shorts,
blue jersey, and smart scarf to match, topped with
a military type beret — John quickly became a
leader of his little group. Ian Boundy, a son of the
Boundy's, who had practically started the church
from the cottage Sunday school days at Ditton
Fields — joined, giving a blessing to his parents
on knowing that their son was following them into
the church. He too, like John Pilbeam, quickly
established himself as a devoted Juno, ever willing to help other boys into the group.

News of the new boys' clan quickly spread. In
less than no time, eighty boys had filled the ranks
of the Campaigners. Margaret Cox, the girls'
chief, gave Pimbo many little wrinkles on handling the administrative side. The ordering of uniforms, collecting the payment of same from the
parents was, at times, quite a head-ache. Some
mothers, hitting hard times, became lax with
their payments, some dropped out altogether, but,

somehow, Pimbo and Jenny managed to equip most boys into uniform.

One evening, Jenny surprised Pimbo. "The uniform business is becoming a stumbling block — there's a bit of tittle-tattle going around — I think it needs sorting out!"

Pimbo looked up from the Juno's programme chart that he was bringing up to date. Jenny went on. "Several boys come from very poor families. We have one boy, that, before joining us, was roaming the streets. His parents seem oblivious to the fact that their son might feel embarrassed at not being like the others, with a smart uniform!"

"I know the boy to whom you're referring!" replied Pimbo. "He comes straight off the streets into the Clan. He's never tidy, his shoes never cleaned. But, he's a lovable lad, I wouldn't want to lose him, if someone drops out, he can have their uniform — does that answer the tittle-tattle problem?"

Jenny smiled wistfully. "Not quite! It goes a little deeper than that. A very tiny majority seem to lose the fact that the ultimate reason for running the Campaigners is to introduce Christ into the lives of the youngsters, and to gradually lead them to make a commitment for themselves — I've heard snide remarks about 'sorting out the sheep from the goats'!"

Pimbo looked puzzled. The lad in reference was a member of Jenny's group. But, as Campaigner Chief, he had, of course, had dealings with the boy at assembly and Clan 'C', the closing prayer session.

"Maybe we are inadvertently causing the problem ourselves, maybe, in our cup awards, we encourage the sifting of sheep from the goats?"

"How come?" asked Jenny.

"Many mothers supervise their son's appearance before leaving home for the Junos. Now, we run a competition for the best appearance, and the smartest boy over the month. It's not fair for the lads from the more apathetic homes, with parents that can't afford uniforms, and take little pride in their offspring's appearance!"

"So what?" smiled Jenny, thinking of the cups which Pimbo had won as salesman-of-the-year, and had given to the Campaigners for award purpose.

"Well, isn't our method a kind of sorting the chaff from the straw? From now on we'll run a competition for the best triers. The lad you mentioned will get a consolation prize as the boy who never misses attendance unless he is ill, or has no shoes to come in — which is quite often!" added Pimbo.

"And the church gossipers?" said Jenny, with tongue in cheek.

"Let 'em gossip. Mr Bowen used to say, 'if it's a lie — it doesn't matter, if it's true — well, it still doesn't matter' — we'll leave it at that!"

After Pimbo had left for a special Betterwear meeting, and with the children in bed; Jenny got to thinking. Meeting many of the Juno's parents made her realise how much devotion was handed out to the youngsters of today. Apart from the minority, whom they had just discussed, most mothers tried hard to give their youngsters as good a life as possible. Maybe 'a land fit for heroes to live in' had not quite come off — but parents certainly made up for the lack of support from Government sources.

Dear Mrs Goulty, with her invalid son, was ever willing to help with the washing up, a bundle of energy, so pleased that her son, Richard, could join in the adventures of the other normal boys. So it was, with most of the boys mothers, supplying a little extra for outings, camps, and sporting equipment. Mesdames, Lawson, Taylor, George, Hurrell, Kitchener, Goundry, Hopkins, all chipping in when it mattered, making sandwiches and collecting jumble.

Then, neighbours Rolls, — Arthur loaning money to equip the boys band with flutes. Millie acting as sitter-in, when Pimbo and Jenny were called away to District meetings.

Tom Ainsworth, now joining Pimbo as deputy chief, was proving to be invaluable with his wonderful way of getting most out of the boys discipline-wise, and enjoyment-wise. Pimbo had now set his sights on forming a Craftsman group, which would ultimately lead to Tom's promotion to Juno Chief.

Then, too, came the idea to provide, each week, the old people from Ditton Fields with food parcels. However, there came a slight hiccup on this seemingly excellent scheme.

Tom Ainsworth, as an Insurance man with the Prudential, had a round which embraced most of the Ditton Fields and outlying areas such as — the Westerings, Peverel Estate, and, of course, the Keynes Road district. He was telling Pimbo, "Our parcel's scheme is going well, people are saying how much good it's doing the Juno's to realise that they are helping out the meagre pension allowance of the old folk — but!"

Pimbo looked up at Tom's slight frown. " 'But', I don't like the sound of 'But' — give it to me slowly Tom, I can take it!"

"It's the old, old story, invidious comparisons. Some busy-bodies are pointing out that a few of the old people receiving parcels have daughters who are working, and should be able to support their own parents. Others, alone, and without kith or kin, are losing out, they receive nothing; but see from their windows the young Juno's taking food parcels to their neighbours — that's how I got to know — news travels fast!"

As the two men were talking, Pimbo noticed two Juno's — Roger and Barry Bagstaffe, during the slight lull in training, wrestling at the front of the church, both on the ground, they had at their head the Campaigner's flag, and a large Cross at the altar. The words of the hymn came to Pimbo's mind, 'Fighting beneath the banner, fighting beneath the Cross!'

"Thanks, Tom!" he answered smilingly. "We're learning all the time. 'Campaigners' is the right word, everything we do in future we must think out. OK, we'll vet the old people — and start again, the snoopers have a point!"

With Jenny's able assistance as Deputy, the Clan grew, not only in numbers, but in all round competence and achievement. Came the day when the new Clan was to be ordained into the Campaigners whole movement. Colonel Wilson, the overall Chief of the Boy Campaigners was to officiate. The Colonel was a wonderful character, fitted with a false arm from his elbow; he oozed charm, grit, and a loving relationship with the Lord.

After the passing out examination, during which both Pimbo and Tom had to undergo drill routine, admin. questions, and show a knowledge of the movement as a whole — came the actual ordination service!

Being Boy Junos' Chief, Pimbo participated in the service by reading out the lovely Psalm 104. As Pimbo read from the lectern, he studied the faces of the youngsters looking up at him. He wondered how the boys would fare as they grew older. Would they ever experience a war similar to his? Would they ever become unemployed to a point of distraction? He read on: He watereth the hills from His chambers; the earth is satisfied with the fruit of His works. He causeth the grass to grow for the cattle, and herbs for the service of man; that He may bring forth food out of the earth. He appointed the moon for seasons; the sun knoweth His going down.

Pimbo's eyes rested on the faces of the girl Junos. He could visualise their going through the same pangs of life as Jenny. Might they find happiness in their marriages? The Campaigner movement would prepare them for the life ahead. He read on: O Lord, how manifold are thy works! In wisdom hast thou made them all; the earth is full of riches. So is this great and wide sea, wherein are great things creeping innumerable, both small and great beasts.

'They shall mount with wings as Eagles'

thought Pimbo, as he finished reading, 'Bless thou the Lord. O My soul, Praise ye the Lord'.

Mount with wings as Eagles! What a lovely thought, and as Pimbo gazed on the smaller children who were not old enough to become Junos — he welcomed the rumour that very soon the Campaigners movement would be finding room for the six-year-olds as Eaglets, or Young Eagles.

After the service, in which many parents attended whose children were not Campaigners, Pimbo received a few applications from older boys wishing to become Campaigner craftsmen, this, a special section for older boys.

Around this time, Paul Leboutillier, a young fellow from Ditton Fields, had been showing a great interest in the movement. With a nickname 'Bootlace', Paul had a keen sense of humour, and Pimbo quickly realising his potential, making him leading craftsman, and responsible for creating a happy relationship between his peers and the Chief.

Paul and Ian Boundy became firm friends, and with Alan Mason, Derek Cornwell, Michael Middleton, and Richard Haynes, formed a nucleus of good fellowship among the new clan.

Several boys came from the Ditton Fields area, and although the Fields, may not, on paper, seem a rich source of recruitmanship — Pimbo soon found that *no* area had a monopoly over another, when character was sadly needed.

Paul was always the last boy to leave the hall after Campaigner sessions. He would help his chief to lock up, and turn away undesirables bent on mischief. That particular session had been almost a disaster, louts had hurled abuse at the youngsters, climbed on the roof of the chapel, and caused unrest among the new recruits, indeed, Pimbo had feared that, maybe, next week would find his Craftsman scheme an absolute flop!

On their way to Pimbo's home, a few hundred yards away, where both would chew over the problems of the evening, Pimbo turned to Boot-lace, "I'm letting you in for something beyond your years, how do you feel, do you want to opt out?"

Paul's young face smiled up at his Chief. "I'm an old St George's boy. Mr Duckering, my old head-master, was known as Just — meaning, of course, justice. He would want me to go on, to prove that his old boys and *something* going for them. I'm wearing a smart uniform, but I want to live up to the Campaigners motto 'they shall walk, and not faint, they shall run, and not be weary, they shall mount up with wings as eagles'!"

"That's my boy!" Pimbo said, as he let Paul into the kitchen. "Do you know, our Commander-in-chief, Colonel Wilson, lost his arm in the war — it didn't stop him from taking on a wonderful com-mitment to make young boys into men — I reckon, we two, with good arms, between us, ought to make something out of our lads?"

Jenny listened intently as Pimbo went over the evening's events. She realised that at one stage of her life, she had never dreamt that one day, she would be instrumental in teaching young people the best ways of living a fruitful life!

God had, indeed, led them in His own mys-terious way. She glanced at Paul, whose East road

*"Fighting beneath the banner,
fighting beneath the Cross!"*

days, and the little misfortunes which had already befallen him — was now ready to take on all-comers, including the ruffians who had spoilt the session.

Jenny remembered from the Psalm, which Pimbo had so nicely read. 'I will sing unto the Lord as long as I live; I will sing praise to my God, while I have my being'!

CHAPTER 16

Moffatt

During the course of Craftsmen teaching sessions, run in the Unwin's home; Pimbo and Jenny found a good friend in the person of a young academic, whom they quickly dubbed 'Moffatt'.

Moffatt was a serious-minded fellow, who had studied Christian Theology, and had volunteered to take the Craftsmen's group in their weekly bible studies. Very small in statue, thin, with a lean look, the young man would arrive with a huge pile of books, from which at almost every sentence of the study, he would ferret out various translations meaningful to the text. Indeed, so exacting were his forays into the translationary books, he, then and there, received the nick-name of Moffatt; also, at times, after a particularly heavy bout of investigations, he would be unable to find to where the translation belonged.

One night, Moffatt, although not in a bible session, called at the Unwin's. "I'm like Nicodemeus, calling furtively in the night!" he half explained his presence.

Over a cup of coffee, Moffatt got down to business.

"I feel that people regard me as a bit of a crank, at the last bible session, I overheard a boy call me a loner — he said I ought to let down my hair — what do you think?"

Pimbo looked across at Jenny. "You're doing a grand job as a bible teacher, however, at times, you seem to be *too* serious. Our boys come from various backgrounds, they regard all teaching as incidental to their way of making the most of their young lives; remember, a number of boys have failed their Eleven-Plus, to them, you are an ex-college boy, doing what you have been taught at college — you see, the boys *expect* that of you, but they would *love* you to show a more natural side to your character!"

Jenny butted in. "We call you 'Moffatt', but we mean it in a nice way, you see, Moffatt, as you know, dedicated his whole life to bring lucidity to the bible — but, I feel there is no need for you to beat your way through the undergrowth, to a path that has already been pioneered — do you ever feel that you might like the company of a nice girl friend?"

Moffatt blinked through his heavy spectacles. "It's funny you should say that. My mother used to say of my room, 'too tidy by half for a boy, you're going to be an old fuddy-duddy, an old bachelor — you mark my words! How do you think your father met me? Mind you, I don't want to put you off your studies — but all work, and no play — you know what they say — !' "

Jenny smiled. She was thinking of her own courting days, how proud she felt as arm-in-arm, they walked the regular walk of the 'monkey parade' in Petty Cury. Then again, perhaps more than ever, as Pimbo and she walked with their pram along the shopping centre in Burleigh Street. Pimbo used to say that, as boys, marriage to them was akin to being in bondage. "Look at his face, a married man out with his wife, shopping — why, he looks as miserable as sin!" was the hearsay of most unattached youngsters. But, Jenny reckoned it was the lack of money, the utter poverty, that caused it.

"Well, what do you suggest, then?" asked Moffatt, appealingly.

"There's a Sunday School treat on the agenda!" replied Pimbo. "The Campaigner girls are joining in with the boys. We've hired a special bus, we go for a ride in the countryside, then finish at Barley, near Royston; where we picnic, and have fun in a field, loaned for one day by a Baptist farmer — how about you coming along — it'll be a rare chance for you to let your hair down, and wear casual dress at the same time?"

Jenny nodded happily at the suggestion. Should Moffatt play his cards right, there were plenty of nice young girls in the Campaigner section. As in the Songs of Solomon, 'Faint heart, never won fair lady!'

On the day of the outing, Moffatt turned up, looking, as Pimbo and Jenny realised, determined to make a go of it! Gone was the trim, pinstriped, business-type suit; in its place, a natty, open-necked shirt, with a slogan emblazoned on its front — 'Chase Me, I'm All Yours'! But the crowning feature of Moffatt's transformation, was his American style head-gear. White, with a bright blue peak, the actual peak went way out, almost concealing his eyes. A pair of smoke coloured sunglasses, and a rattle, as used in football matches, completed the picture. Wide, flared denim jeans, put Moffatt on a par with any young man on the outing, with a veiw to making the aquaintance of a female companion.

"Hi-yuh!" said Moffatt, as Pimbo greeted him.

The young man spent most of the journey standing at the rear of the bus. A few stragglers had been picked up en-route; these Moffatt helped on, with a cheerful "Hi-yuh", and a swirl of the rattle. The bus sped on, through Shelford, Harston, and then to take up the more picturesque side roads leading to Barley. Several times, Moffatt started up a spate of choruses, 'I'm H.A.P-.P.Y', 'Give me Oil for my Lamp', and old favourites, such as, 'Wide, Wide as the Ocean'.

Jenny sensed that Moffatt was, indeed, enjoying himself. At times she caught the looks of some of the senior members of the church. Head down, side-long looks, and little cupped-hand whispers, to be followed by wry smiles, which told of their acceptance of Moffatt's unusual role.

Jenny thought of one of Moffatt's own little texts, wherein St Paul stated that he would, 'become as all men — in order to witness for the Lord'!

With the Sunday School outing reaching its destination, Moffatt moved across to a young Clan deputy chief, whose main task was that of assembling a group of children to prepare for a set of games.

The deputy, a pretty dark-haired girl, Jenny

knew very well as Jean Noble, living in Ditton Fields. Jean had become a Christian some months ago, and with the blessing of her mother, had committed herself to working with young people, hoping that, through her witness, they might seek faith in Christ!

With the children handed over to their respective leaders, Jean had time on her hands.

"You're doing a grand job!" said Moffatt, smiling hopefully.

Looking up, Jean smiled back. "I like your outfit, quite snazzy. I've heard about you, they tell me that you teach a fair bible-study?"

Moffatt blushed. "You mean, they didn't make fun of me?"

"Why should they? I work in a bank. You should see *me* at work. Stern-faced, looking down on a set of figures, as though they were about to become unruly! Do you know, should I relax, become too free, well — I couldn't do my job. I suppose some customers, with large overdrafts, might not take too kindly to some of the letters I have to endorse. You see, Moffatt, yes, I know they call you 'Moffatt', bible study *is* a serious business, the same as banking!"

"That's very kind of you!" stammered the young man.

Jean rose to her feet. "You can take off that silly hat, remove those smoke-screen glasses, and I'm sure that the advice given in Ecclesiastes, 'A time to laugh, a time to cry, a time to dance, a time to die' can be heeded by you, as well as your young pupils! Come on, we'll go for a walk before tea!"

The young couple smiled as they watched

merriment going on in the spacious field loaned by the generous owner, Mr Parsons, the Barnwell Sunday School superintendant, from the back of a tractor, pursued by a swarm of happy children, was throwing, willy-nilly, handfuls of sweets, out to the lucky recipients.

"They won't want any tea!" laughed Jean. "By the way, what does your dad do for a living?"

Moffatt blushed for a moment. "I was brought up in a children's home, I don't know my parents. My foster parents have been wonderful, they put me through college, perhaps that's why I try so hard, in order to repay them!"

"My dad's a fireman at the local cinema, the Victoria. As a hobby he grows beautiful plants, and a ready supply of fresh vegetables. Mum hasn't much time for anything other than bringing up a large family — but, she's very clever with the needle!" answered Jean.

Now the children were well into the sack race. The young couple stopped to help out with minor injuries, as over-eager participants fell over.

With the tea now being taken, Jean moved across to assist Jenny with her group, as Moffatt helped Pimbo with the junior boys. "A nice lad!" Jean was confiding to Jenny, as she, with bright enquiring eyes, was looking at Jean; ready for a report on her little encounter with Moffatt. The point concerning the foster parents, and childrens' home, caused Jenny to reflect on her own childhood.

Kempston Childrens' Home, at Bedford, had been Jenny's home for several years. A bed-ridden mother, although kind and loving, couldn't cope with a large brood of boys and two girls. 'Dad' White, as Jenny called him, did as much as a father could do to keep the family together. An old war veteran, and thus, a devout British Legion man; 'Dad' spent many happy hours in the 'Legion' hut. Jenny, in those days, was 'spokesman' for her brothers' and sister, in the Kempston Home. Many times she ran home to her mother in St Leonard's Street, to tell of any injustices meted out by an over-strict Matron.

'Dad' White would then plomp mum into her wheelchair, and the pair would remonstrate with the unkind Matron.

Jenny's later connection with Cambridge was that 'Dad' White eventually moved to Cambridge, living in Russell Street. His work with Panton Brewery, culminated in *his* being the original patent, for bottling beer. On 'Dad' White's death, Jenny, like Moffatt, was taken over by a Cambridge family, and thus to meet Pimbo as a childhood sweetheart!

You're day-dreaming!" broke in Jean, as she laughingly stopped Jenny from over-filling a glass with lemonade. "You were miles away — I suppose you were contemplating a love match with myself and Moffatt?"

Jenny blushed. "Of course not. But I think you did very well. There, you see, he's removed that silly hat, and seems to be more at ease, now he's back to his normal self!"

"We're going to be good friends. He's taking me to a concert at the Guildhall. We both have something in common, when it concerns folk music. Nina and Frederick's 'Sea-Shell', is one of

Moffatt goes on the Sunday School treat!

our favourite loves — Moffatt, I can assure you, isn't as stilted as he might appear to others!"

The rest of the day, Jenny spent with Pimbo, mustering and re-mustering their small charges into manageable groups. At times, they would glance across to where Jean and Moffatt were busily helping out with the washing-up chores. They both seemed thoroughly at ease in each other's company.

On the way home, Moffatt, minus his hat and sunglasses, lead the youngsters in lustily sung choruses. Somehow, Moffatt seemed to accentuate the last lines of an oft-repeated chorus — "I know I am, I'm sure I am — I'm H.A.P.P.Y.!"

CHAPTER 17

Going Into Business

Cambridge was spreading its wings. The after-math of war, with its bristling, home from the wars young men, was most conducive for young men to go all out to make up the deficiencies in their own childhood. Charles Barham was talking to Pimbo outside his little factory premises at No. 2, School Lane. Charlie was one of a family of well-known brush manufacturers. Pimbo well re-membered queueing for a bag of shavings at Charlie's dad's place in Coldham Lane; hoping, that among the wood shavings, there might be large enough pieces to use for kindling a fire.

"You're a good salesman!" Charlie was saying. "Why not come in with me? I make the brushes, you sell them. I have six good girls working for me — maybe you and me could go places?"

Pimbo got to reckoning. He wondered whether Charlie was big enough to guarantee a regular supply of enough brushes, variety-wise, to satisfy the insatiable appetite of dust-conscious house-wives.

"My firm replace all deficiences!" answered Pimbo. "We do all colours, I doubt whether you'd be able to compete with such a large monopoly. Anyway, how *are* things with you, are you doing OK on your own, since you broke away from you dad?"

Charlie smiled, wistfully. "I came back from the war full of ideas. Do you know, Pimbo, I picked up a lot during the war. I always was a man with a social conscience — the war enhanced an already growing germ, in other words, I wanted to see that workers got a fair deal. Pimbo learned later of the little brushmaker's final demise!

Charles was the first on the market with a special brush for distributing tar on to roofs of sheds, paths and other building attachments. Starting in a small way, he supplied several shops, sold a few to casual customers from his factory, and was gradually building up to several score a week. Charles rewarded his workers with a pay rise.

One day, an influential sales rep. spotted the brushes in one of the local shops. He was so attracted by the quality of the brush, the price, and its potential for sales outside Cambridge, that he paid a visit to Charlie's factory.

Charlie was only too pleased to show how the brush was made, the technical intricasies involved, and his method of preparing the raw material for the finished article. "I can sell hundreds for you!" the rep. told the delighted brushmaker. "We can come to financial arrangements, as soon as we get sales on a firm basis!"

The 'firm basis' turned out to be gross after gross of weekly orders, from all over the country. So much so, that poor Charlie found that the cost of raw materials to cover the innundation of orders, was far beyond his scope. Charles put the unhappy position to his would-be benefactor!

Don't worry, get your raw materials, and send the bills to me!" came the reply.

One day, the shock came! "You owe me a substantial amount of money. I want it within seven days!" The benefactor had turned into a greedy money lender!

The brush-maker was dumbfounded. The money for brush sales had yet to come in, to pay the amount demanded would finish him for ever as a business man!

"Within two days, I registered into the Bankruptcy Court!" lamented Charles to a friend. "I was done for, I looked on the fellow as a kind of 'Angel', you know, the chap that backs a stage-show. I really thought that as money came in from sales, we could come to amicable arrangements. But I put it all down to inexperience, I suppose my old dad must have gone through similar hell!"

On hearing the sorry tale, Pimbo thought again of his own little experiences. The 'brush-off' covered so many literal occasions! There was the up-and-coming car salesman, ironically, with a sleazy garage in School Lane, a few yards from Charlie's brush factory.

Before making his final purchase of the beloved Austin, Pimbo had made inquiries as to the likelihood of getting a bargain at the School House Lane garage. During the war, many young lads had opted into the REME, a quiet haven; where stopping a bullet could be put well out of mind, and at that, perhaps, a trade in motor mechanics, be placed against one's name!

Pimbo was shown a very large car, looking very much the worse for wear. "You'll see your face in it, Mate!" was the confident ring in the salesman's voice. "A good clean up with Simoniz, we'd have done it, but the car's straight from the last owner — to you!"

Walking gingerly to the passenger side of the car at the salesman's offer of, "Jump in, I'll give you a spin!" — he noticed the door was almost off its hinge! "Hang about! I'll have to lift it well clear — it'll drop in, you see!"

The salesman followed his words with a terrific heavo, which almost turned the car on to its side.

With a splutter and shudder, the car lunged its way on to East Road. "Better hang on to the door, Mate, going round corners it might swing off, can't afford to lose a customer, can we, Mate?"

A thick belching smoke was coming from the rear of the car, each time a gear was changed came a sound of searing metal against brass!

"Well, what do you think to it, Mate? A nice little crate, eh? Goes like a bomb. I'll get in a welder to fix the door, the neighbour's will think you've won the pools, there you are, fifty quid, including free air for the tyres!"

Pimbo was one of the world's worst buyers. Jenny would often chide him over this weakness. "You go into a shop — and it's the first thing they show you, 'Yes', you say! Why don't you compare?"

Looking down at the gear lever, and other instruments, Pimbo thought of Jenny's words, 'why don't you compare?' Well, in this case — there was *nothing* to compare with such a heap of rubbish. 'Goes like a bomb' he'd said. Pimbo half expected the whole contraption to blow up any minute! 'Free air into the tyres' — he doubted whether they would stand any more pressure, without capsizing!

As they drew into the side of the School House Lane garage, a seedy-looking individual came from inside the garage, carrying a dirty, greasy-looking rag, which he proceeded to wipe across the windscreen of the car. "We hope to get a show-room one day, go a bit up-market, if you see what I mean!" he explained, as he produced a filthy dog-eared log book, from inside the interior of the car. "One owner, used to take his old mother to church on Sunday — week-end driver. Packed away during the war — you've got a snip, Mate, at fifty nicker!"

Pimbo couldn't help it. He burst out laughing! Packed away during the war! — It must have been the Boer War! One owner! — *who* the hell would buy such a wreck?

"I'll think it over, Mate!" said Pimbo, between fits of giggling. "On second thoughts, count me out. I don't want to have you on a piece of string — you'll need all the string to keep the car from falling to bits! Sorry Mate, not quite what I had in mind!"

"Saucy sod!" Pimbo heard the salesman say, as he moved away. "Getting too big for their boots nowadays — I don't know what they expect for their money!"

But of course, in this day and age, there was a lot going for second-hand stuff. Hammond's auction room on Fridays. Anderson's little shop in

Fitzroy Street, always good for a buy. Endersby, Warwick, household names for the old hands. But, for the new generation, it was new — or nothing!

Funny thing, thought Pimbo. Post-war Cambridge seemed to have developed an atmosphere of its very own. The car shin-dig he'd gone through, might well have ended in violence. Before the war, he would never have been so flippant or rude, even the salesman was happy with just 'saucy sod', as a kind of last word on the matter. Then again, Charlie's 'put it down to experience' philosophy, was scant reward for his unfortunate financial loss. Pimbo reckoned that the public were using their war experiences against any set-backs in their lives. Just like a battle, some we win, some we don't!

Life was changing. Churchill had just died. Humphrey Bogart was dead. Pimbo remembered in one of his films 'High Sierra' — 'It's organisation, that's what we want! Think every move — you guys rush into things. Stop to think, how do you think I got where I am? You're just lousy bums, I can't afford to carry dead-wood. You, Leftie, take Shorty outside, when I hear a shot, I'll know how organised *you* are!'

Young men were starting up little businesses of their own. Pimbo had noticed on the market, the one in the centre of town; a stall solely for shoppers to deposit their bags and parcels, for an in-turn delivery to their homes. A smart white van, labelled 'Home Deliveries', was standing aside, awaiting customers. Poor old Jim Wooders, never dreamed how his pioneering effort of 'looking after your parcels, Madam' — for 2d or 3d a throw — might mushroom into such a business venture.

Jim, with his little hunch-back Charlie sitting alongside Christ's wall in Drummer Street, never made a packet, just enough to get by on. Pimbo hoped that the Home Deliveries van would go from strength to strength.

Then again, we had the Proctor brothers, making a go of furniture removals, now with a large van, proudly displaying their name. Mr Duckering, their old head-master, was really proud of their achievement.

Harvey Cornwall, Jnr. — following his dad's illustrious footsteps — 'footsteps' perhaps not the correct word; whereas Harvey, Snr. — *walked* his way into Cambridge homes, his son used an up to date van for his flourishing business in Mill Road.

The Cooper Bros., emerging from horse and cart into 'Here Comes Cooper' emblazoned on the front of their removals van, into a hard-working successful venture into the furniture trade.

Pimbo smiled as his mind went back to his short stay in Caldicote, a small village on the way to St Neots, then known as Tin Town. The village shopkeeper, Mr Sparks, very eccentric, with spiky hair (in those days), would cycle into Cambridge on an old trade bike, load it with fish from McFisheries, then cycle back in order to justify the sign on the grass verge of his shop — 'Fresh Fish Daily'!

Pimbo reckoned that a lot of young men, with a memory of the thirties in their mind, were trying desperately to make something of themselves. At one stage, he and Jenny had almost decided on taking up his own brush trading firm. A look in 'The Exchange and Mart' showed prices ridiculously low, but on their visiting the warehouse, they felt that the goods, although cheap, would not bear comparison with those of Betterwear, he certainly could not guarantee replacements!

Then too, folowing Mr Newberry's sally into a round's business, we had 'Les', with his large grocery van, covering the huge estate around Pimbo's home. To eke out a living, Les could be found among the cluster of council homes as late as 10.30 p.m. With the war over, Les no doubt sank a large proportion of his savings into his venture. After a very good try, and bags of hard work, Les was swallowed up by the large grocery monopolies — a nice chap was Les!

Smilingly, Pimbo recalled how in liaison with a close friend, he attempted the window-cleaning business. "See how you get on, Mate. If you can cover a good days work, you and me can set up as partners!" his would-be ally had put forth.

Pimbo found window-cleaning far from being the doddle it was reputed to be. His first mistake was to worry too much about the corners. With Jenny's criticism in mind over his home attempts, he decided *not* to ignore the corners. Then, chatting to customers did nothing for his day's output. "So you're new then?" "The last man only charged 1/- for the bottom windows!" "Fancy a cup of tea, I've just made one?" "You run the Boys' Campaigners, don't you? My little grandson wants to join, I'll give you his address!" "My old man had a go at the window cleaning lark, had a job to get his money, he chucked it in!" — and so it went on.

Losing a lot of time at one house, caused a flurry at the next, with a slight loss of Pimbo's initial thoroughness.

Finding a place to put his ladder, caused minor rumpuses with the garden-conscience neighbours. But, the deciding factor, had to be his aching muscles! In the morning he could hardly raise his arms shoulder height. All this, too, in the summer, with nice sunny days! Thinking of the winter ahead, Pimbo called it a day!

Starting up in business, without sufficient capital, trying new ventures, was put into the background when he arrived home. "It's Keith, he'd like to start work instead of staying on for another year!" Jenny greeted him. "What do you think?"

His son was a bright lad. Already, he was pitting his chess prowess against graduates at different colleges. Sport was his great love, and although he did reasonably well at lessons, his heart wasn't really in prolonging school life for yet another year. Christine had acted in similar vein. Nursing had attracted her, and after passing a preliminary exam, she commenced her working career by becoming a Cadet Nurse at Fulbourn Hospital; with sights set on a Students course when reaching eighteen, with the usual General and Midwifery certificates to follow.

Mr Aldiss, Gent's Outfitter of Rose Crescent, Cambridge was the venue for Keith's launching into the tailoring trade. Amazingly, Pimbo's first local job at fourteen, was as an errand boy with a tailoring firm just a few hundred yards away in Trinity Street. His son, however, was going one better, he wanted to be a shop salesman.

Both Jenny and Pimbo had accompanied Keith on his first job's interview. Although reluctant at first — "It makes me look like mummy's boy! They don't do it, dad, like they did years ago!" — Keith soon found that his father's reminiscing over the war years with his future boss, might help toward his being appointed!

"We do a good trade here!" pointed out Mr Aldiss, in a gruff voice, which moulded in with his still splended physique. "We're the only shop in town holding a genuine Levi's certificate, so we cater for both young and old clientelle!"

Almost to prove his words, an elderly man from the country entered the shop. His wife, a tiny woman, piped up, "He's come in for his usual, Mr Aldiss. Vests and long johns, you know — the kind he always has!"

Smilingly, Mr Aldiss, with the aid of steps, pulled down a draw from the top of a large array of boxes.

"There you are. Three buttons down the front of the vest, and ribbed sleeves, short — if I remember!" With a nod from the old pair, the shop owner wrapped up the goods.

"Been coming in for more years than I can remember. The old fellow wouldn't buy a vest without three buttons. I have to make sure they're the same make!" Mr Aldiss told Pimbo, as the couple left the shop. Then, turning to Keith, "The customer is always right, boy. I've built up my business through knowing what the customer wants. I get fancy rep's coming in here with new lines. One button, two buttons, sometimes no

"We hope to get a show-room one day — go a bit up market — if you see what I mean!" said the car salesman.

buttons at all — but I always have the old boy in mind, and that goes for everything else!" Pausing for a moment to view Keith's acceptance of his manifestations, giving Pimbo a sly wink, he went on.

"Do you still want to work for me?" You've got the job, I run a farm in my spare time. On your day off, you may come up — maybe earn a bob or two — how about it?"

Noticing a boy his own age, peeping from behind a kind of partitioned-off tea-room, and Ralph, the manager, with an enticing smile; the row upon row of shirts, ties, socks, sweaters, trousers, the newly fashioned jeans, and the crisp smell of new clothes, the busy hub-hub of the town centre, with on-off noises from the nearby market, pitting all this against the thought of another year of maths, geometry, and chemistry — Keith nodded. "Yes, Sir, I'd *like* to work for you!"

A SOLDIER RETURNS TO CAMBRIDGE

Cambridge from Liverpool Street,
The fields and trees so neat,
The eyes of a soldier, as he lands
Fresh from hot African sands
Rest on the view, one of a few,
Alive and well, come home to tell.

Station's the same, a taxi, a talk,
"No thanks, take my time, it's better to walk".
Devonshire Road, down Kingston Street,
Joan's Number '8', hope we don't meet
'Till I've been home, cause Mum and Dad must,
Be like in Norfolk say, they come 'fust'

Sturton and New Street's, getting near now,
Coldham's Lane compleating the vow
To return someday to Silverwood Close,
'63', the place I love most.
Aunt Con's there, to open the door,
My knees are jelly, I can't feel the floor.

The hugs, kisses and lips in a pout,
From all my body, the desert ran out.
I was home, I was home, Oh beautiful place,
Surely my tears could be no disgrace,
For King and Country that's where I'd been,
My heart, these people, that's what I mean.

by Charles Barham (the ex-brush maker)

CHAPTER 18

Lancashire House

Money in the Unwin household was getting tight! On the strength of Jenny's coming to the conclusion that her job in the toy shop was little more than pin-money; she'd decided on taking a new job as a catering cook. The venue for this change of fortune was Lancashire House. This establishment was a boarding house cum-restaurant for a host of lively young language students.

Situated in Hills Road, it lay back from the main road, so as to become indiscernible to anyone not knowing of its presence. Language schools were popping up like mushrooms, affording a lucrative income for anyone with enough foresight to see the financial potential for suchlike ventures.

Sprinkled among the legitimate schools, were bad apple monstrosities, giving inadequate teaching facilities, with poor premises. Gradually, these were being weeded out, but, as in many cases, a few were slipping through the net.

Cambridge people, at first, took none too kindly to the young language students. They seemed rude, showing scant respect for adults, some appeared far too young to be on their own in a strange land. A regular feature, on the streets of Cambridge, was a group of chattering students blocking the pavements, and thinking nothing of queue jumping in front of the most senior of citizens.

Jenny was given an interview prior to her engagement. Mrs McGovern, the manageress, cum-hostel keeper and administrative clerk, put it to Jenny.

"This is a hard job! You'll have to be mother, cook, and general adviser to the youngsters. I shall expect you to order all raw materials for your cooking requirements. One thing, you must stick to a limited budget. My present cook is a finger-picking fancy Freda! All show and little substance; but, her bills are enormous, yet the boys stay ravenously hungry — do you think you might make an improvement on that?"

Jenny smiled back at her potential employer. She was thinking of a staff-sergeant cook in her old ATS Unit. Although they were not the best of pals, and unaware of each other's home town; to her surprise, Jenny discovered that not only was the ex-Sgt. living in Cambridge, but, was holding down a job as chef at a leading Mill Road restaurant!

"My ATS experiences will see me through!" replied Jenny, brightly.

"Well, then! You may start on Monday, I'll take your round the kitchen, you can acquaint yourself with the new-fangled cooking utensils!"

'Finger-licking Freda', a slim Norwegian girl, was busily preparing the morning lunch, as Jenny entered the small but efficient looking kitchen. On a long range, Jenny noticed about a dozen small saucepans, all simmering merrily; with Freda every now and again peeping under their lids, in case anything might try to escape.

"I'm a lover of sauces!" explained Freda, in broken English. "I study in Norway, I have a degree! Bechamel Sauce, Brain Sauce, Chaudfroid Sauce, and Hollanaise Sauce — you name them! One day, I will open a restaurant on my own. Already I have my very own sauce, Maitre D'Hotel Butter, it will make me a lot of monies — but you English do not understand my art — you think too much of Fish and Chips, and Daddy's sauce!"

Out of earshot, Mrs McGovern explained. "She drives me mad. The boys turn up their noses to most of her dishes. One day she came up with her own concoction of a sweet. It looked and tasted like hair-cream, Creme-de-Luxe, she called it!"

Jenny could hear the buzzing chatter of the students as they rushed in for morning coffee, and a biscuit. The manageress trotted off into her small office at the rear of the hostel, leaving Jenny to wander around the building. Lying around on the tables, she spotted text-books of varied subjects — 'Living English Structure for Schools' by Longman. Teach Yourself Books; 'Common Sense English' by F. T. Potter, and the 'English of Business' an American-servicemens' book, by Gregg.

Jenny reckoned that by 1975, language students would be coming to Cambridge in great force. There was money in it; already there had

been a rush to bring many of the schools up to
standard. A long-fought out case in the local
paper, was nearing its end, in a dual between
teacher and school, as to the standard of lessons
involved.

It seemed that some students, from wealthy
parents, used their time at language schools for a
holiday period; English lessons were mere in-
cidentals in a merry-go-round of social events.
This gave the go-ahead for sloppy-lessons needing
fewer qualified teachers — but, happily, this was
now on the wane, with only the first-class schools
able to survive the strictest of tests!

Also, with the inundation of extra visitors to
Cambridge, agencies were plying ordinary house-
wives to board the students, offering good pay to
successful applicants. Then, too, colleges were
breaking into the scene, offering classrooms, and
in some cases, full-board during vacations!

On the strength of watching the tiny morsels
which Freda dished out, thus leaving the students
clamouring for more; Jenny decided on giving
man-size meals, using good old plain puddings
that, hopefully, filled!

For tea, she made a large fruit cake, which she
cut into portions — this turned out to be heart-
breaking!

Came five o'clock, a mad rush into the dining-
room; as the students swarmed over Jenny's cake
portions, in a few seconds, the special treat had
been swallowed up! Happily, the boys appreciated
Jenny's cooking, but it made her feel as though
she was trying to fill up bottomless pits, not
stomachs!

Mrs McGovern, after a week or so, told Jenny that she was well pleased with her work. "I'd like to get a little place — somewhere away from Lancashire House!" she confided one morning, during her coffee break. "Living on the premises is bad for my nerves. I hear the students late into the night, sometimes I take a little scotch to help me doze off, but I'm afraid that I might well become addicted to it — have you any ideas?"

Jenny, sipping her coffee, wracked her mind. Accommodation in Cambridge was getting tight. In the fifties, a grand scheme on the Arbury Estate, resulted in a score-or-so hard-working neighbours banding themselves into a building group, and constructing their own homes — but, this of course, was no help to her boss. Jenny suddenly thought of Miss Dorris Forbes, the lady from Lynwode Road, whose lawn Pimbo had set out from the pre-fabs to cut! "There's a chance, a slim chance, of you perhaps sharing a large house with a friend of mine!" replied Jenny. Anxious not to build up Mrs McGovern's hopes too highly, she added. "I'll pop round on the way home, maybe I'll have something to tell you inh the morning!"

Remembering Pimbo's description of the house, and she herself having worked in Lynwode Road, made it quite easy for Jenny to find her way to Miss Forbes' door. Making her way to the back door, she noticed how untidy the garden had become since Pimbo's little gardening effort a few years previous. Some time elapsed before the door opened. Miss Forbes, red-eyed and pale looking, stood motionless, as Jenny introduced herself. "Come in!" she said meekly. "But I'm afraid I cannot offer your husband a job — you see, my sister has died, I'm all on my own — !"

A slight sob came to her lips, as she offered Jenny a chair. I'll make you a cup of tea, my dear. How is your little girl, she must be almost grown up by now?"

"You've been crying, Miss Forbes. Is there any way in which I can help?" Jenny noticed the untidiness of the place, the little tell-tale bits such as — a calendar with the previous month still intact, a few weekly newspapers, still unread, as picked from the letter-box.

Doris seemed to have brightened up since Jenny's arrival. Wiping her eyes with a tissue, she sat more firmly into her chair. "I'm very lonely, and I'm worried about the upkeep of the house. You see Jenny, I'm not well off, my sister, to my surprise, had so many unsavoury friends, that the bulk of the money she left, has been taken up with the payment of her debts — for me, there was nothing! On top of that, there are discrepancies in the mortgage payments, making it almost impossible for me to sell the house!"

Jenny smiled warmly. She then explained to Doris, the reason for her visit. Jenny pointed out how near to Lancaster House was Doris' house, and the kindness shown to her by Mrs McGovern, also telling of the good lady's own problems.

Miss Forbes listened intently. "It seems that you have been sent by God, my dear! The money would solve a good deal of my problems — but, do you think she would like my place enough to share expenses? It seems too good to be true — but there is one set-back! You see, of late, I've lost heart;

I've let the place go, as you can see; I'm no dab-hand at cleaning, I could never get the place round in time for Mrs McGovern to inspect it?"

Jenny was thinking of the ten-shilling note which Doris had given Pimbo, at a time, too, when Jenny's purse was empty.

"I'll help you. I'll bring up my entire family, we'll all muck-in, we'll have this place ship-shape in no time – one thing, though, can I use your 'phone, I'll ring up Mrs McGovern and tell her the good news — ?"

The Lancashire House manageress was delighted at Jenny's telling of her meeting with Doris, and its conclusion. "Put her on the 'phone, I'd like to talk to her myself" she implored.

As Jenny left to bring along Pimbo and the children to help out; she heard Doris happily confiding with Mrs McGovern, and seemingly, coming to some arrangement over the financial side of things.

Luckily, Keith and Christine were available, and loading up the Austin Seven with buckets, brooms, and other cleaning requirements, the Unwin's set off for Lynwode Road.

Keith and Christine had plumped for tidying up the garden; leaving Jenny and Doris flipping through the lower rooms, while Pimbo took on the upstair apartments.

"My, what a lot of cookery books you have!" exploded Jenny, after humping the umpteenth volume through into the small box-room. "Whatever do you do with them all — some are years old?"

Doris, now almost her old self, smiled. "I love

cooking, it's the only thing I can do well. Since Alice went, I'm afraid I slacked off a bit, but now I'm raring to go, from now on, it's me slaving over a hot stove!"

After several hours hard slog, the house took on a semblance of its old look. Pimbo came downstairs, carrying several brushes which he's found stored away in an old cupboard. "Betterwear brushes, almost new, must have been here for years, worth a penny or two, I can tell you!"

Doris was beaming as she made them all tea, at the end of the cleaning session.

Suddenly, the bell rang. Doris, laughingly, looked across to Jenny. "A little surprise, I gauged how long our clean-up might take; I invited Mrs McGovern round, I couldn't rest until we'd finalised our little deal!"

The Hostel Keeper took an instant liking to Doris, who, in turn showed a similar pleasure at meeting her potential home-companion.

"What a lovely place, my dear. And only a stone's throw away from Lancashire House. I'm going to love this, and it's all happened so quickly, just like a story book. I'm sure that we both can be happy together!" beamed Mrs McGovern.

Jenny stood up from the table. "I think, peerhaps, you two would like to have a chat in confidence. As instigator of this plan, I feel that, perhaps, I've rushed things a bit — er, you know what I'm trying to say; its not fair if you don't take a long hard look at each other talk things over and do it all off your own bat — I'm sure that you understand!"

With Keith and Chris on their way home, Pimbo

and Jenny, whilst the two ladies were discussing their future, looked out from a top window down on to Lynwode Road.

As a milkman, Pimbo had many trips into this area, not much had changed! The Pickles family, with son at the Perse, dear old Carlton-Brown helping everyone she could, with her faithful little servant, Peggy. Miss Briggs, always with a lovely wreath on her door over Easter. The Churches', now a little frailer. Tom Cash, now passed away, Pimbo's old school-chum, who did sterling work at the Gas Company, only to die, almost on retirement!

Pimbo pointed out to Jenny, the corner which led into Tenison Avenue. It was there, that his friend, taking his moped exam', with his examiner awaiting his return from opposite Du-pont's building, had knocked over a careless pedestrian, re-mounted, and carried out the stipulated route, (all unseen by the examiner), to pass with apparent honours!

On the day his licence arrived, a summons also turned up in the same post!

A noise from downstairs, told the young couple that the conference was over.

"It's all stitched up!" said a smiling Doris. "We got on like a house on fire, after a while, we're going to use this house in similar vein, to that of Lancashire House. That way the upkeep of the house can be maintained, the mortgage squared, and Phyllis here, yes, we're on first-name status, can be in charge!"

Then with an added rider, Doris went on. "I'm going to be head cook, you see, Jenny, my books

"Finger licking Freda", was preparing the morning lunch.

will not be wasted! And, for you, when once we open up, will be a regular job in charge of bed-linen and arranging cleaning staff!"

Phyllis was smiling, as Doris finished her gentle tirade. "Yes, Jenny, we'll carry on until I've managed a new contract with the Language School, I know they're crying out for new premises, Doris and I have been more lonely than one might think, I thank you, Jenny, for what you've done for us both, and your husband, of course, who, Doris tells me, is a jack-of-all-trades!"

Pimbo, in his *mind*, added the old adage 'master of none', but refrained from spoiling the compliment!

Doris was seeing Jenny and Pimbo to the door. "Phyllis is staying for a chat. This is a great day for me — an answer to my prayers!" said Doris.

As the young couple moved down the pathway, they noticed what a good job Keith and Chris had done with the garden. To their surprise, Doris was still behind them; at the gate, she shook hands with them both, then turning to Jenny, said almost wistfully, "I think it was Voltaire who said, 'All the glories of this World, are not worth a *good* friend'!"

There was no answer to that, thought Pimbo, as he watched Jenny's modest smile of appreciation.

CHAPTER 19

Such Is Life

The years were passing. Keith was becoming established in his sales-assistant's job at Aldiss's. Christine was doing well in her nursing venture, having graduated from Cadet Nurse, to that of student-nurse proper! At Barnwell Chapel, things too, were on the move, Phillip Withers was proving to be a fine Minister, and the little chapel was being blessed by the Lord.

"I hear Moffatt is leaving Cambridge!" Jenny was telling Pimbo. "Going in as a missionary, he's a fine young man, we certainly shall miss him!"

"And Jean Noble?" broke in Pimbo. "How did she take it, I mean — had she really fallen for him?"

Jenny smiled. She knew in her heart, that Jean was such a lovely girl, full of compassion, Moffatt's going would be regarded by Jean as the work of the Lord!

"Jean has made friends with Malcolm Finch, there's a strong rumour that they are about to become engaged — we shall see!" said Jenny, with a coy smile, as though Pimbo should already have known.

Pimbo chided himself at not keeping up-to-date with the romantic side of Barnwell. Jenny was a past master at match-making. Malcolm was the son of Bdr. Finch, Pimbo's old Troop Clerk in the 8th Army days. The Bdr's sudden death had brought Gwen, his wife, down to the chapel, where Jean Noble first met Malcolm. Pimbo guessed that Jenny had been more than a little instrumental in furthering the romance!

The little chapel then went through a spate of misfortunes in regard to their parishioneers. Mrs Twigwell, the dear little woman, who worked so hard to give John and Jean everything that she herself was unable to get in her own childhood, died suddenly. Bill, her husband, a delicate man throughout his life, soldiered on with his work at Marshall's.

Coming home from work to an empty house, Bill scurried around, lighting fires, preparing meals, for two hungry youngsters on their return from school. After a long period of such-like stress, Bill's blood pressure heightened, eventually causing his sudden collapse and death. Even with the help of kind neighbours, and loving relatives, Bill was unable to carry on!

Tragedy struck again with the death of Tom Ainsworth, Pimbo's Deputy Chief for the Juno's. Tom, an ex-prisoner of war in Burma, had suffered great hardships from both a physical and medical view. His ultimate death was a legacy left by the terrible Railway of Death.

Tom was well loved by all who come in contact with him. The Juno's adored him, and his death left almost an impossible gap to fill!

The Girl Campaigners received a shock in the departure of Miss Chewter, their Chief. Miss Chewter, a teacher at the same school as Miss Cox, (the older girls' Chief), was leaving to take up a teaching post at another school. All this, however, was allayed by the bubbling presence of a new recruit in the person of Barbara Seebrooke, who kept everyone alive with her jolly personality.

Barnwell Baptist, during an Evanagelical campaign, gave Pimbo and Jenny a chance to offset the recent tragedies befalling the little community.

It was in a small Close, quite near the chapel. "Come in, my dear!" invited the little rosy-cheeked woman, in reply to Jenny's — "We're from the Baptist Church in Howard Road, it's our recruitment drive, we'd like you to know more about our chapel — !"

The little council home was well furnished, and the lady of the house put on the kettle as means of a special greeting for the two church workers.

Noticing a photograph on the sideboard of a young girl who Pimbo immediately thought of as Juno age, he made his play. "Your daughter's very much like her mum, I must say! We have a very good group of Juno's, your little girl would have good company, be able to go to week-end camps, and yourself, could join in our community activities?"

"I'm Rose Clinton, yes, this is my daughter, Rosalind, I'd very much like her to join with youngsters of her own age!" Placing Rosalind's photo back on the sideboard, she went on. "It's funny that you should choose my house to visit, I would think that of all the homes in this Close, mine might well be the unhappiest!"

With promptings from Jenny, Mrs Clinton told of a slow breaking up of her marriage. She had an elder daughter, as well as Rosalind, both girls were at loggerheads with their father, whose apparent distancing himself from their mother, had caused great distress in the family. Things were getting at such a pitch that Mrs Clinton spent much of her time in tears, the loss of respect from her husband was in no way due to any marital misdemeanours by herself, and for that matter, neither did she feel that her husband was two-timing her in any way!

"It could be your husband's age!" put in Jenny, kindly. "Men do go through a climacteric period, akin to a woman's menopause, have you thought of calling in the Social Welfare — they could help, you know!"

The woman smiled. "I don't wish to appear cynical, but my faith in social workers is not very great. I've carried on hoping that perhaps it's just a bad dream, that one day it might all go away. It's my children I worry about, their life now seems to be drained of all quality; they are little better off loving-wise, than if they were orphans!"

Jenny was thinking how different it was in real life, than that of the vows taken at the marriage altar — 'Until death us do part', 'In sickness and in health'. But, she couldn't throw the book at them! People outside the church just didn't understand. They use the church at weddings, births and funerals, but it was like living in a gold-fish bowl, immune from the practical world of real living!

"Would you like us to have a chat with your husband?" asked Jenny at length. "Perhaps a third party might do the trick — how do you think he'd take it, my husband would be willing to tackle him on his own?"

It was agreed that Pimbo would have a meeting with Mr Clinton, then, should anything come of it, a second meeting, including the whole family group, would take place in the hope of a final settlement — one way or the other!

Pimbo found Mr Clinton to be a well-built, healthy looking man, in his early forties. "My wife told me about your little agony-aunt games. I can't see what good you can do, my love for her seems to have gone, that's all there is to it, although we live together, I go my way, and she goes her's — in any case, I can't give you much more time — I'm really still on duty!"

From the window, Pimbo spotted a small mini-bus, which, on his coming in, he had failed to notice, it was parked opposite the Clinton's home.

"Yes, I work for the Health Authority, pick up the kids from their homes, take them to Coldham's Lane Children's Work Therapy, then bring them back again!"

Pimbo remembered that one of his Juno's was in the group that went each morning to the Coldham's Lane centre. "You do a good job, then! One of the Juno's parent's can't thank you enough for what you are doing for her son — you help to bring him real happiness and something to live for!"

Clinton shrugged. "It's just my job. I might just as well be carrying parcels — don't give me any credit for what I do!"

"I don't believe that. You're being modest, what would you say to someone who, however indirectly, brought happiness to *your* two daughters, it wouldn't be the same as carrying parcels — I'm sure?"

"What are you getting at? I guessed that you do-gooders, would try some trick! Trying to get at me through my children — eh?"

"It's a fair question!" replied Pimbo. "What do *I* get out of it, other than seeing your daughters getting what they should be getting from their father — another thing, it's better to be a do-gooder, than a do-nothing!"

Mr Clinton looked at his watch. "I'm due at the Centre in ten minutes time. I must be getting soft in my old age, like to come along with me? Maybe you're right, I don't really look upon them as parcels, I couldn't do it year in and year out. You got my goat, made me feel guilty — we'll talk again later!"

The mini-bus drove in at the entrance to the Coldham Lane Centre for Mentally and Physically handicapped personnel. As Mr Clinton helped seeing the youngsters aboard the bus, Pimbo recognised several whom he had seen at their homes, when on his brush round.

The Day Centre was indeed a boon to harassed parents. Their off-spring could spend a whole day with people who had a similar affliction to that of their own. Most were of varying ages, giving a fair balance of discipline, in that the older ones could help out against tantrumatic behaviour. Also, some of a higher status could earn a little money, giving them a feeling of rare accomplishment!

Mr Clinton was thoughtful as he drove home his passengers. Silverwood Close, Ditton Fields, Newmarket Road, the Peverel Estate, all came within his range.

"The staff at the Centre — are grand!" Clinton was saying. "I couldn't do their job for a pension. You should see them when the kids really let loose — patient as old nick!"

Pimbo, having helped a youngster off the bus, sat next to the driver. "You can call me Bob! There, you see, you've broken through my barrier. I suppose you're going to ask me how lucky I am to have two normal kiddies?" finished Clinton.

"We're communicating — that's the answer really, Bob! How long is it since you spoke to your family, hear both sides, I'd say, then go from there!"

Bob was silent for the rest of the journey, on reaching the Close, having dropped off his remaining passenger, he looked up at Pimbo. "We'll talk, come round tomorrow night, there'll be the missus, the kids and myself. You two biblepunchers, can see fair play — how about that?"

Jenny was very pleased at Pimbo's disclosures. After Pimbo had left with Bob Clinton, she had stayed wtih Mrs Clinton for some time. "Rose seems to have a good deal of faith in us. She feels sure that it was more than the arm of coincidence that brought us along — she has Christian beliefs, and feels that Bob, too, deep down, has more than he pretends!"

Pimbo was thoughtful. How was it that in such a short time, they had been able to make *any* progress at all? The marriage of the Clinton's had been crumbling for some time, yet, two apparent strangers had at least got them talking again!

"Do you think they're leading us up the garden path, I mean, it seems too good to be true. After the meeting, they might go back into their shell?" asked an anxious Pimbo.

"Oh, ye of little faith! We must wait and see; but I have a little plan, which may well bind them together, once they accept the fact that they have no *real* issues to tear them apart!"

"I'll go along with that! Do you know, Jenny, I think old Bob started by cutting his wife off from his thoughts, that, in the end, he got so confused, he was unable to get back on the rails again!"

The meeting with the family of the Clinton's went so well, that after a pause in which to celebrate the coming together of the family unit (with a little sherry), Jenny dropped the surprise packet which she had promised her husband to deliver.

"I've had a long talk with Mr Withers. He's agreeable to participate in reuniting of Mr and Mrs Clinton — in other words; he thinks it quite appropriate, that you be joined together again, in marriage — a kind of confirmation of your burying the hatchet — so to speak!"

To Pimbo and Jenny's great surprise, Bob and Rose were agreeable. In fact they both indulged in a loving embrace, as their two mediators left, a trifle embarrassed, to tell the Ministeer that the re-marriage was on!

And so it was that Barnwell Baptist Chapel took its first marriage ceremony. The little building was full on the great day. Many relatives from both sides turned up, making it a day to remember.

With the reunion over, Pimbo and Jenny were ruminating on the events which had threatened to overshadow many of the happy occasions that Barnwell Baptist had been through.

"I was thinking how many broken marriages could be repaired, if they were as sensible as Bob and Rose!" Jenny put to Pimbo.

"Not everyone gets a second chance! I suppose marriage, is like going into business, things can go wrong, and if you are not equipped for trouble, well, that's all part of life — like a stage, really!"

Jenny pointed to an item in the evening paper. The New Theatre, the only music-hall in Cambridge, was closing down. "Talking of stages, and getting a second chance, there goes my little Friday night excursion into the 'good old days' — remember?"

Pimbo nodded. Jenny loved the music-hall. One performance, had Davy Kaye inviting children on to the stage. Christine, then only 2½ years, sang 'Buttons and Bows' and the 'Little Dutch Mill'. Davy Kaye had picked her up in his arms, and carried her to the edge of the wings for Pimbo to collect both she and her prizes. In his doting father excitement, Pimbo fell flat on his face, to the amusement of the audience — yes, the New Theatre had pleasant memories for him!

Then, too, was the long winding stone stairs, where he as a young lad, would climb, to watch John Wayne and Gabby Hayes, in almost their first film, they were known then as the 'Three

*"Your daughter is very much like her mum!" pointed
out Pimbo.*

Musketeers', Pimbo couldn't remember who the
third man was! (Dick Foran, maybe!)

Jenny went to the variety performances, where
Max Miller, Benny Lee, Max Wall and many
others would take part. The orchestra knew her

quite well; a wife of the violin player, would invite Jenny round to tea at her flat in Clarendon Street. It was during such trips that Jenny learned of the pitiful wages paid in those days. The violinist received just 30/- weekly. Such is life, thought Jenny.

CHAPTER 20

Baptism

"Unto Him — Through and Through'

Barnwell was growing. The old orchard area, which once prevailed, had mushroomed into a large sprawling estate. The children of the Ditton Fields residents, were settling into new homes, leaving aged parents to ruminate over the long gone days of one-up-one-down little houses; where, as many as eight in a family, were reared, and brought into society.

Pimbo saw many of his school friends come up the hard way, and yet make the grade. Don Murfet, a youngster always interested in choral activities; through pursuing this channel, Don moved from one progressive stage to another, until reaching Civil Service status, and due respect from all he came into contact with.

On the other hand, there was Mr Doggett, ex-Newmarket Road, now living in Pepy's Terrace, Histon, whose musical career started at eight years of age, as a bugle boy with the Salvation Army. Mr Doggett, thought his SA bugling days were over when he left the SA Cambridge group to live at Histon; where, apparently, this group did not realise his years of loyalty, and failed to cash in on his services. Happily, he found his niche with the nearby Impinton band — and all is well! Mr Doggett still owns instruments used by the Cambridge SA band dating back eighty years.

"It's fixed!" said Jenny, suddenly, breaking into her young husband's day dreams. Jean and Malcolm are getting married at Barnwell church. You're best man, and Christine will be a bridesmaid!"

"So you've done it again, match-maker supreme, well, I'll say this, a better match I've yet to see. Who have you set your sights on for the next wedding?" laughed back Pimbo.

The little Austin was getting past it. Reluctantly, Pimbo decided to sell it, and procure a bigger car. However, when it came to the bitter crunch; he somehow just couldn't take money for a car which had absorbed the love of two owners. Even then, the young student to whom Pimbo had given the car, wouldn't drive it away, until he'd pressed £8 into Pimbo's hand. "Out of sheer respect for the old gal!" he said, as the recent owner almost tearfully watched him drive away into the busy Newmarket Road area.

A Morris 1000 was Pimbo's next choice. "A good clean little car!" said the salesman from Abbey Auto's. "Nice chassis, good suspension, not too renowned for acceleration — but, then you're not one of those speed merchants, are you?"

"I'll have it!" said Pimbo, signing the proffered documents, for easy-term payments. As he was left alone with the Morris, standing resplendant outside his home; Pip Smith, a neighbour who also was a bus-driver, came up.

"What's the engine like, Pimbo?"

Pimbo blinked. It seemed incredible, that in the trial run, the sales chat, and the 'looking over' of tyres and body-work, he had failed to scrutinize the engine!

Pip Smith smiled knowingly. "You amateurs are all the same, make it easy for the con-man!" After lifting the bonnet, and picking about the interior, Pip nodded agreeably. "You've got beginners luck. It's a nice job — nurse your engine, and you've got a good few years motoring there!"

After he'd gone, Pimbo was telling Jenny about the incident. "Well, you know me, Jenny. I always did think a little knowledge was dangerous — !"

Jenny was in no mood for compromise. She was thinking of the time when Pimbo drew into a garage because he felt the car wasn't pulling well. The attendant laughingly pointed out that a flat front tyre might well be the cause of the sluggish performance!

Then again, complaining about lack of pulling power at another garage, the attendant, on lifting the bonnet, was met with a cloud of billowing smoke. It was a rug which Pimbo had placed over the engine against a severe frost marring instant starting!

The Campaigners were moving from strength to strength. Mr Hopkins, a neighbour a few doors away, had, in the loss of Tom Ainsworth, helped out by taking the boy Juno's in knot practice; being an ex-Navy man, he was well versed in splicing the main brace, and his sea-faring tales went down well with sea-conscious lads. His daughters, Elizabeth and Diane, were already Campaigners. Jenny was talking it over with Pimbo concerning the new baptism pool which Mr Jack Twinn was building for the little chapel. Mr Twinn was one of a large family of Christian folk, which had roots years back, to the days when Great-grandfather Twinn had taught Pimbo in the Nelson Street mission hall.

"I think it time that we consolidated our faith in Christ!" Jenny put forward. "Mr Twinn is working hard on the baptistry, he reckons it will be finished within a month. Miss Cox would like a special Baptismal Service with the Campaigners taking a leading part!"

Pimbo nodded. As with Jenny, his childhood had been one that had accentuated all the things with which faith had been tested. His TB days, his war-time experiences, he work with the Campaigners, whereby meeting Colonel Wilson, Miss Cox, Miss Miller, and many others; now, the spiritual essence of Christianity, had spilled over into their lives, bringing something akin to that which Christ had promised, 'My Peace, I leave unto you, a *Peace*, that the world understandeth not'!

So Pimbo and Jenny took up a course of pre-baptismal teachings which would lead them into the Baptismal service arranged by Phillip Withers to take place within the ensuing month!

On the great day the little church was packed. The Minister's sermon prior to the baptism, stressed on the wisdom of not looking at the emotions, and try not to test your spirituality by your feelings. Do not study *yourself*; look away from self to Jesus! As many as received Him to *them* gave He power to become the sons of God.

Mr Withers went on: Every Christian should study the Bible because he *loves* it; not to develop a habit of depending on commentaries, concordances, and other aids — aim to make the Scriptures your *own*, in this way can you become possessed of Light, Power, and Love.

> Read them; but first thyself prepare.
> To read with zeal and mark with care.
> And when thou read'st, what here is writ
> Let thy actions second it.
> So twice each precept, read shall be —
> First in the book, and next in thee!

Mr Withers, during the singing of the lovely hymn — 'Just as I am, without one plea; O Lamb of God I come'! left the altar in order to prepare for the actual baptismal ceremony.

Pimbo, dressed in white shirt and white flannels, watched intently as Phillip Withers emerged from a side room, wearing a white shirt, and a huge pair of waders similar to those worn by fishermen. He took his place firmly and confidently in the centre of the baptismal pool, which hitherto had been expertly covered by specially-made slotted framework — the work of Mr Twinn.

Now it was Pimbo's turn to be dipped and submerged in the baptismal water. A symbol of being buried in the old sinful ways, to emerge, washed and cleansed, to arise a new being, as Christ Himself rose from the dead. As Mr Withers leaned Pimbo back into the water, his head entirely submerged, Pimbo actually had a feeling that, indeed, something had been left behind in that baptismal water. As he arose, blinking against the strong light, recovering his breath from a mouthful of water, with anxious hands ready to help him up from the depths of water, to embrace him with spiritual grace, and envelop him with warm comforting towels, Pimbo sensed that he *had* indeed, become a new being, washed in the blood of the Lamb!

Still bemused with the lovely strains of the baptismal hymn, echoing in his water-filled ears, Pimbo was led to the improvised dressing room laid on by Miss Cox!

Inside, his mind went back to a little reading, he couldn't remember its source, it was thus:
Seek the clasp of Christ's hand before every bit of work, every hard task, every battle, every good deed. Reach out your arms to the dewy freshness of every morning, before you go forth to meet the ardours of the day. Wait for Christ to lay His hands upon you. Their touch will inspire you for courage, and strength, and all beautiful and noble living!

Pimbo was glad, because he knew that Jenny, too, would be experiencing the same wonderful feelings he had been through. Then too, Paul Le-Boutillier, Ian Boundy, Alan Mason, were subjecting themselves to a similar ceremony, where young lads from the Ditton Fields area, too, could become as one in the Lord.

Dressed, but with his hair still damp, Pimbo rejoined the congregation to sing out lustily the closing hymn; with Jenny standing by his side, clasping his hand, as though in recognition of the fact that as man and wife, they too, had consolidated a faith, which had begun during the rigours of a poverty-ridden childhood, and had taken them into the little Baptist chapel at Barnwell!

With the joys of the Baptismal Service well in the past, Barnwell was to suffer another spate of tragedies. Mr Twinn, after his strenuous efforts in finishing the baptism-pool, succumbed to a heavy stroke. Despite several remissions, he was unable to throw off the final attack.

Mr Hopkins, just as he was becoming a very popular figure in the Juno parades, became very ill, and to the utter despair of his loving family, passed away after a brave fight against a terminal illness.

Another blow to the Campaigners was the surprise death of their beloved Chief, Jean Noble. After her happy marriage with Malcolm Finch, Jean, following her husband's admiration for the motor scooter, also took up riding the then popular machine. An accident in the Cherryhinton High Street, gave poor Jean terrible head injuries, from which she was unable to recover. Jean's death left a big gap in the Campaigner's Chief's list. She was one of the most beloved people in the Barnwell community.

The youngsters in the Junos found it very hard to accept so many tragic events. Pimbo and Jenny, in their 'Clan C', during which, time is taken to reflect on recent happenings, and to offer prayer, used the occasion to remind the Clan that God giveth life, and also taketh away. Only He can fully understand the reason.

The Sunday School at Barnwell was growing.

Pimbo and Jenny had become teachers, with the Ridgeon brothers, Michael and David, also teaching, and Mrs Isherwood from the sister church St Andrews, officiating as Junior Superintendant, with Mr Parsons as Head Superintendant.

With the failure of the food parcel scheme well in mind, Pimbo and Jenny put to Mrs Isherwood, a scheme in which the junior members of the Sunday School could take part. In lieu of classes, the children would actually leave the building and visit the old people living in the Ditton Fields area. Mrs Isherwood, ever alert to find new ways of putting over the Christian message, readily agreed.

The first Sunday of this new innovation was fine and sunny. Mrs Isherwood, with Pimbo and his class of juniors, made their way into Ditton Fields.

It was with a little trepidation that Pimbo approached the small bungalow housing the old lady who had been chosen for the first call. "Come in, my dears!" was the pleasant surprise greeting the little band. I'm very lonely, you know. You're my first real visitors for many a moon!" Whilst Mrs Isherwood was explaining the reason for the visit, Pimbo took in the furnishings of the little home. On a sideboard, amass with sepia photographs of many years standing, were tiny china ornaments, little trinkets with names such as 'Present from Hunstanton'. A whole generation of life, depicting the loves and strifes of yesteryears. Hard-working faces, standing at the portals of tiny unhygienic homes, with stand-pipes as their only means of water, usually prominent in most pictures.

Small children, with white pinafores, but equally white faces, looked out from the frames, as though afraid of what the 'dicky-bird' was really about!

Little Mrs Cook, bright-eyed and busy, trotted about the little home, showing off her tapestry work, the lovely patterned hand-stitched designs; then it was outside to the small flower garden. Inside once again, the little widow took out an old tea-tin from her cupboard. The picture of Queen Victoria filled one side, as she pulled out a few sweets, handing them around to the children.

"You will come again?" almost pleaded the old lady, as the little party prepared to leave. Jenny found out later that Mrs Cook's husband had not been one of the best, in her widow's years, with the childrens' visits, the old lady had found a new happiness!

Mrs Isherwood, on her way back to the Chapel, expressed her delight at the success of the visit.

"But it mustn't stop there!" put in Jenny. I suggest that each class adopt an old lady. It doesn't just take place on Sunday; during the week, the children, without making a nuisance of themselves, visit daily — do her shopping, and in general make her life a little less lonely.!"

So it came about that the Campaigners, the Sunday School, and the church members took it upon themselves to make life easier for its parishioners.

"It's a new awakening!" Pimbo was saying to Jenny as they reached home. "You can't say that we old service-wallahs aren't doing what we used to gripe about — 'an England fit for heroes to come home to'!"

Jenny smiled as she thought of Christine doing her bit as a nurse. Keith, too, had received good praise from Mr Aldiss — 'Best salesman I've had for years'.

Pimbo, too, had even tried his hand in the political field. Using his car to transport voters from Ditton Fields to the polling booth, by nine o'clock, zero-hour, there were still hundreds left! Mr Shelley, a grand old railwayman from the Abbey Ward, with a record of his sons also being the back-bone of railway service, was the candidate for the Abbey Ward — he lost by one vote!

Thinking of the many voters he was unable to pick up, Pimbo smiled wryly. "Oh, the things that might have been!"

However, the following year, Mr Shelley made amends with a victory, winning the Abbey Ward with a good majority.

Keynes Road children grew into fine young teenagers. Houses changed hands, as through hard work and diligence, some were able to purchase new homes.

The sudden death of Pip Smith threw another shadow over Barnwell, but Pimbo was meeting new friends as he travelled the streets with his brushes. Old friends too, in the person of Clem Leonard, another lad from the St Paul's vicinity, embracing Russell Street, Coronation Street, and the famous Cambridge Place. Clem made his way through the bad old thirties, finishing as a teacher, and taking great interest in local educa-

It was Pimbo's turn to be submerged in the baptismal water.

tion, with his brothers in like progress.

The death of Jack Twinn, brought to mind the old Nelson Street Adult School cricketing days. Jim Laughton, opening bat, the Challis brothers, and dear old Mr Whybrow, Sonny Kirkup, real triers all!

"You're getting old!" laughed Jenny. "Thinking about the past, you don't get we women at it, we're too busy looking after the family!"

Pimbo smiled back. Maybe she was right! the old faces were like the little puzzles he attempted as a child — 'How many faces can you spot in the picture?'

The older he became, the faces were a little fewer, some he still spotted, standing with their sticks at the corner of the street — watching the clouds roll by!

FORTIETH ANNIVERSARY

(Pimbo and Jenny celebrated "theirs" on 8th September,
1985)

I rejoiced at my wedding, some forty years since,
When Pimbo was happy, and proud as a Prince.
It was a whirl of a time, but, whatever the cost,
I'm happy to say the memory's not lost!

The Keynote was Love, ushered in with a Kiss;
And a matter of fact, the feeling was bliss.
I heard from the lips of a pertinent friend,
How I scoffed, when they hinted it might quickly end!

And has it? Of course not; marital problems we've
      nursed,
And I venture to say, we're happy, as at first;
That is, if we had to be choosing again,
We should say, "Well, the pleasure will cover the pain!"

But, you see I'm a mother, and mothers who work,
Have many a problem, which others can shirk.
And when there are plenty of bills on the mat,
One doesn't expect, everything to be exact!

And I must understand, and try to be kind,
When the amount of our income is on the decline.
Nor question a fault, which, might well be mine,
If it's pouring with rain, when *he* wanted it fine!

He thought I was **this**, and I thought he was **that**;
Which, of course, was a little mistake — to be pat;
Life's just as good now, as it was when we married,
Though we wouldn't have altered our mind, had we
tarried.

But, he loves me, I know, from the bottom rung,
And we talk, as we talked, when we were young.
It is natural, of course, for flowers to fade,
But love's fragrance remains, though its rose is
decayed.

Fred Unwin

*(This poem is dedicated to those whose marriage
coincided with the termination of the 2nd World
War).*